ADVANCES IN COMPUTER CHESS

1

M.R.B.CLARKE

Editor

Edinburgh
University Press

© 1977
Edinburgh University Press
22 George Square, Edinburgh

ISBN 0 85224 292 1

Set by Speedspools, Edinburgh
and printed in Great Britain by
The Scolar Press Ltd,
Ilkley, Yorks

CONTENTS

PREFACE

This is an appropriate time to inaugurate a series of meetings devoted entirely to computer chess. Of course chess and computer science have had a long, if at times superficial, association since Turing and Shannon formulated the basic principles on which a program could be written, but until quite recently improvements in the standard of play could be attributed more to better hardware and increasing ingenuity at what has been called the 'bit-twiddling' level than to any significant advance on the Turing/Shannon model.

Within the last few years however it has been seen more clearly that chess epitomises many of the problems with which the wider field of artificial intelligence now defines itself as being concerned—the storage, representation and retrieval of knowledge, and the use of it to create more knowledge. Many of us would maintain that chess, with its simple representation yet deep structure and richly developed culture, may even be the best system in which to study these problems in their purest and most readily quantifiable form; and that a symposium to take stock of the new work of this type that is beginning to emerge is particularly timely.

The idea of such a meeting, together with many of the suggestions that made it a success, originated with Donald Michie through the Artificial Intelligence and Simulation of Behaviour Study Group (AISB), whose committee underwrote a share of the finance. However it would scarcely have been possible without the generous and wholehearted support, both financial and organisational, of the Science Research Council's Atlas Computer Laboratory, its Director Dr Jack Howlett, and Marjorie Sherwen and Alex Bell who bore the brunt of the organisation. ICL helped with travelling expenses, Balliol College kindly provided tranquil and civilised accommodation, and the final word of appreciation must go to the Edinburgh University Press for their efficient and seductively produced record of the proceedings—we hope the first of an increasingly compulsive series.

v

On the Structure of an Important Class of Exhaustive Problems and Methods of Search Reduction for them

G. M. Adelson-Velskiy, V. L. Arlazarov and M. V. Donskoy

This paper discusses the necessity of structuring a search tree. A theorem is stated that the $\alpha-\beta$ algorithm is the only search reduction procedure for non-structured minimax problems. For a class of problems structured in some way a non-trivial search reduction method is described.

INTRODUCTION

In most problems of artificial intelligence an exhaustive search is an important (we think, a main) method of choosing a solution among certain alternatives. The central problem, which arises here, is that of search reduction without prejudice to the quality of solution. A search reduction is called absolute if the search graph is certainly lessened, and it is called heuristic if reduction of the search graph depends on good luck. (We do not consider here search reduction techniques which may lead to the loss of solution, although they are sometimes also called heuristic.) The subject of the theory of exhaustive search (considered as part of artificial intelligence theory) should be, naturally, heuristic search reductions. In this connection the following problems arise: that of formalisation, that of inventing a search reduction method (heuristic), and the problem of analysis of the reduction method. An analysis consists apparently of the following parts: an applicability domain, uniqueness results (under such and such conditions no other method exists), results on optimal effect, examples of the absence of effect, and results on 'rentability' of a method, whether the time spent to answer the question 'to reduce or not' is saved by essential reduction of the size of the searched set. In the present paper we choose a simple (but important) case of exhaustive search—namely minimax problems—and the $\alpha-\beta$ algorithm as a heuristic search reduction method, to make a part of such an analysis. We show that if a corresponding method is used for too wide a class of problems, then it is the only search reduction method for this class (more precisely it majorates all other methods). A class is too wide if, roughly speaking, the structure of problems of the class is subject only to trivial restrictions. Example: there is no search reduction method applicable to all cooperative games (a degenerate case, where all vertices in the game tree are maximal).

As a philosophical implication of this result we conclude that to construct a non-trivial search reduction method one needs to use the structure of a problem. A method of search reduction discussed in the second part of the talk confirms our conclusion. It uses a kind of symmetry possessed by some problems. This agrees with F. Klein's general principle according to which mathematics studies symmetries of the world. (However, unlike the situation in geometry, in our case these symmetries do not form a group.)

It is important that this method is compatible with the $\alpha-\beta$ algorithm and supplies essentially different, additional possibilities for search reduction. This method distinguishes our class of problems from earlier classes of problems with restrictions (travelling salesman etc.). In those problems restrictions were used to strengthen the application of the $\alpha-\beta$ method and do not lead to any innovation in it.

NOTATIONS, ASSUMPTIONS, DEFINITIONS

We go over now to a formal description of the problem and of the results. All trees to be met in the paper are finite, directed and have a unique root. If T is a tree, v_0 denotes its root, $V(T)$ (resp. $E(T)$) denotes the set of vertices (resp. edges) of T, End T denotes the set of end vertices. For $v \in V(T)$, $T(v)$ is the tree 'hanging' at v, $EN(v)$ is the set of edges leaving v, $N(v)$ is the set of end vertices of edges $e \in EN(v)$. For v_1, $v_2 \in V(T)$, $[v_1, v_2]$ denotes the (directed) path from v_1 to v_2. Suppose we are given a map $i: V(T) \to \{\pm\}$. Set $V^+ = i^{-1}(+)$, $V^- = i^{-1}(-)$. Suppose further we are given a completely ordered set D such that for any $D' \subseteq D$, inf $D' \in D$ and sup $D' \in D$ are defined (e.g. $D = R \cup \{+\infty\} \cup \{-\infty\}$). For $d_1, d_2 \in D$ we set $-(-d_1) = d_1$, and we assume that $-d_1 \leqslant -d_2$ is equivalent to $d_1 \geqslant d_2$. The letter f denotes always an evaluation function f: End $T \to D$, and F denotes a transition function $F: E(T) \times D \to D$. Δ denotes the set of pairs (F, f) such that F is monotonically non-decreasing with its second argument and, $\forall e \in E(T)$, $F(e \times D) = D$. For $(F, f) \in \Delta$ the function $\phi_{F,f}: V(T) \to D$ is defined inductively by $\phi_{F,f}(v) = f(v)$, $v \in$ End T:

$$\phi_{F,f}(v) = i(v) \sup_{w \in N(v)} i(v) F([v, w], \phi_{F,f}(w)), \ v \in \text{End } T.$$

A function's family $\Sigma \subset \Delta$ is called too wide if the following holds. Suppose an algorithm A is given (with value-set $D \times D$), which for any $v \in V(T)$ and for any sub-tree $T_1 \subset T$ and for any $(F, f) \in \Sigma$ computes sup and inf of $\phi_{F_1, f_1}(v)$ over all $(F_1, f_1) \in \Sigma$ that coincide with (F, f) on T_1. Our condition has the form:

(g1) $\forall (F, f) \in \Sigma$, $\forall T_1 \subset T$, $\forall v_1, \ldots, v_m \in V(T)$ with $E(Tv_i \cap T_1) = \emptyset$, $v_j \notin [v_0, v_i]$ for $i \neq j$, for any choice of $B_i \in [A(T_1, F, f, v_i)^-, A(T_1, F, f, v_i)^+]$, there exists $(F_1, f_1) \in \Sigma$ such that $(F_1, f_1)|_{T_1} = (F, f)|_{T_1}$ and $\phi_{F_1, f_1}(v_i) = B_i$.

If any interval $[d_1, d_2]$, $d_1 \neq d_2$, is infinite, (g1) may be replaced by a weaker assumption of absence in Σ of relations of the equality or inequality type:

(g2) $\forall (F, f) \in \Sigma$, $\forall T_1 \subset T$, $\forall v_1, \ldots, v_m \in V(T)$ with $E(Tv_i \cap T_1) = \emptyset$, $v_j \notin [v_0, v_i]$ for $i \neq j$, for any function $\rho: D^m \to D$, for any sign $\square$ taken from the set $\geqslant, =, \leqslant$, and for any $d \in D$, there exists $(F_1, f_1) \in \Sigma$ such that $(F_1, f_1)|_{T_1} = (F, f)|_{T_1}$ and $\rho(\phi_{F_1, f_1}(v_1), \ldots, \phi_{F_1, f_1}(v_m)) \, \square \, d$.

An *exhaustive search* working on $\Sigma \subset \Delta$ is a rule of walking round T.

Explicitly: it is a computable function $\pi : N \times \Sigma \to V(T)$ such that $\forall (F, f) \in \Sigma$, $\forall n \in N$, one has

$$\pi(n+1, F, f) \in \bigcup_{i \leqslant n} N(\pi(i, F, f)).$$

A *search reduction* or *cut-off* of the search π is a computable function $\rho_\pi : N \times \Sigma \to \{\pm i\}$ such that $\forall n \in N$, $\forall (F, f) \in \Sigma$, $\forall (F_1, f_1) \in \Sigma$ such that $(F_1, f_1)|_{\bigcup_{i \leqslant n} \pi(i, F, f)} = (F, f)|_{\bigcup_{i \leqslant n} \pi(i, F, f)}$, $\forall (F_2, f_2) \in \Sigma$ such that $(F_2, f_2)|T - T\pi(n, F, f) = (F_1, f_1)|T - T\pi(n, F, f)$, one has the implication $\rho_\pi(n, F, f) = -1 \Rightarrow \phi_{F_2, f_2}(v_0) = \phi_{F_1, f_1}(v_0)$. Given a cut-off ρ_π one constructs the new search π' (also exhaustive), which walks around fewer vertices: if $\rho_\pi(n, F, f) = -1$ then for all $i \geqslant n$ such that $\pi(i, F, f) \in T\pi(n, F, f)$ we set $\pi'(i, F, f) = \pi(n, F, f)$. Repetitions may be excluded afterwards.

RESULTS OF THE $\alpha - \beta$ METHOD

The $\alpha - \beta$ method is applied to the problem of computing $\phi_{F, f}(v_0)$. This problem is solved by exhaustive search. Suppose we are given a tree T, a family $\Sigma \subset \Delta$ on which we are working, an exhaustive search (a way of walking round T), and an algorithm A with properties described above. To construct a cut-off called the $\alpha - \beta$ method, we construct at first for $(F, f) \in \Sigma$ the set $T(n, F, f) = \bigcup_{i \leqslant n} \pi(i, F, f)$. Then we construct a system of Bounds $B = \{ A(T(n), F, f)^{\pm} \}$ on functions of Σ. Then we construct the set $V_{BB}(T(n), B)$ equal to the union of trees T_v over those $v \in V(T)$ for which there exists $w \in [v_0, v]$ such that $F([w, v], B^{i(v)}(v)) \geqslant B^{-i(w)}(w)$. Lastly, we put $\rho_{BB, \pi}(n, F, f) = -1 \Leftrightarrow \pi(n, F, f) \in V_{BB}(T(n), B)$. To construct an A one uses restrictions on functions from Σ and explicit computations of $\phi_{F, f}$ in certain vertices.

Theorem 1. If Σ is too wide, then the only search reduction for an exhaustive search π working on Σ is $\rho_{BB, \pi}$ (in the sense that all other search reductions are worse in the obvious sense).

This theorem is to be found, in a slightly different form, in Adelson-Velskiy *et al.* (1970).

Without going into technicalities, let us note another result that can be either deduced from theorem 1 or proved independently. Under the assumption that the number of edges in min- and max-vertices are approximately equal, the number of end vertices in the optimal search tree is not less than $\sqrt{|\text{End } T|}$.

Simple examples of restrictions on Σ: (a) the sum of values of $\phi_{F, f}(v)$ $\forall (F, f) \in \Sigma$ over some fixed set of vertices (e.g. over vertices of the given level) is bounded by a given element; (b) the problem of the travelling salesman: $V^- = V(T)$, $D = R \cup \{+\infty\} \cup \{-\infty\}$, a function $c : V(T) \to D$ (the transport fares) is given, $c(v) \geqslant 0$ such that $F([v, w], d) = d + c(w)$. Then restriction follows from the evident relations

$$F([v_0, v], \phi_{F, f}(v)) = \sum_{w \in [v_0, v]} c(w) + \phi_{F, f}(v) \geqslant \sum_{w \in [v_0, v]} c(w)$$

STRUCTURES

Theorem 1 shows (as we have mentioned in the introduction) that new methods of search reduction should be sought for families Σ distinguished by non-trivial relations.

As a model that (in a reasonable approach) includes all non-trivial restrictions known to us we propose the following schema: let M be a set, possibly endowed with the structure of a partially ordered set or some other suitable structure. Suppose that a map (structure map) $\sigma: E(T) \rightarrow M$ is given. Requiring of F and f a 'good' behaviour with respect to σ and its structure on M, we shall get a non-trivial restriction on Σ. The travelling salesman problem is an example. We come now to a detailed description of an example of conditions on σ, and of methods of applying it to search reduction.

These conditions have naturally arisen in exhaustive analysis of variations in a chess program (Adelson-Velskiy *et al.* 1970).

For chess $\sigma(e)$, $e \in E(T)$, is a move from the initial position of edge e to its final position, considered on the empty board and containing an indication of which piece was captured; M is the set of all moves on an empty board with capture indications. In this case, one has $|V(T)| \geqslant 10^{100}$, $|M| \leqslant 10^4$. σ and M are analogously defined for checkers and card games with exposed cards.

Suppose that V^+ and V^- are interlaced in $V(T)$, i.e. $i(w) = -i(v)$ for $w \in N(v)$. Suppose further that $M = M^+ \cup M^-$, and that for $w \in N(v)$ one has $\sigma([v,w]) \in M^+ \Leftrightarrow i(v) = +$. Let us write $i(m) = +$ for $m \in M^+$ and $i(m) = -$ otherwise. The set of non-empty paths $[v,w]$, $v,w \in V(T)$, is denoted Paths T. Seq M denotes the set of ordered sequences of elements from M (possibly with repetitions) whose signs alternate. Seq M is endowed with the natural structure of a tree and we shall consider Seq M with this structure. Then σ induces the map $\tilde{\sigma}$: Paths $T \rightarrow$ Seq M or, similarly, the map $\tilde{\sigma}T \rightarrow$ Seq M. Suppose that σ^{-1} is unambiguous on edges $e \in EN(v)$, $\forall v \in V(T)$ (i.e. $e, e' \in EN(v)$, $\sigma(e) = \sigma(e') \Rightarrow e = e'$).

Then for $v \in V(T)$, $s \in$ Seq M, one denotes by $v + s$ the unique vertex $w \in V(T_v)$ such that $\tilde{\sigma}([v,w]) = s$ (if, of course, $s \in \tilde{\sigma}(\text{Paths } T_v)$). Let us introduce on Seq M an operation $+$ by $m = m_1 + m_2$ if m is obtained by writing down m_2 after m_1 and if $|m_1|$ is even. We shall write also $m \in m_1 \oplus m_2$ if $m_1 = m_{11} + \ldots + m_{1k}, m_2 = m_{21} + \ldots + m_{2n}, m = \sum_{i,j} m_{ij}$, and if in the latter sum all lengths, except possibly the last, are even.

RELATION OF INFLUENCE

Suppose that on the tree Seq M a relation of influence is given and that a relation of influence of elements from Seq M on elements of M is given. Suppose that the relation of influence satisfies the following conditions (where $m, m' \in M$ and $s, s', s_i, s \in$ Seq M):

Axiom of symmetry of influence:

s influences $s' \Rightarrow s'$ influences s.

Axioms of extension of influence:

$m \in s \Rightarrow s$ influences m

$m \in s$ and s' influences $m \Rightarrow s$ influences s'.

Axioms of the transfer of influence:

s influences s' and $s = s_1 + s_2 \Rightarrow$ at least one s_i influences s'

s influences m and $s \in s_1 \oplus s_2 \Rightarrow$ either some s_i influence m or s_1 influences s_2.

s influences s' and $s \in s_1 \oplus s_2 \Rightarrow$ either some s_i influence s' or s_1 influences s_2.

This relation of influence is extended with the help of σ to a relation of influence in the Paths T and to influence of elements of Paths T on elements of M. For this extension some additional axioms are to hold (where $v \in V(T)$, $w_1, w_2, w_3 \in V(T_v)$, $\tilde{\sigma}([v, w_3]) \in \tilde{\sigma}([v, w_1]) \oplus \tilde{\sigma}([v, w_2])$):

Axioms connecting admissibility of moves and influence:

(a) $\exists m \in M^{i(v)}, m \notin \sigma(EN(w_i))$, $i = 1, 2$, $m \in \sigma(EN(w_2)) \Rightarrow$ $[v, w_1]$ influences $[v, w_2]$

(b) $\exists m \in M^{i(v)}, m \in \sigma(EN(v)), m \in \sigma(EN(w_i))$, $i = 1, 2$, $m \notin \sigma(EN(w_2)) \Rightarrow [v, w_1]$ influences either $[v, w_2]$ or m

(c) $\exists m \in M^{-i(v)}, m \in \sigma(EN(w_1)), m \notin \sigma(EN(w_2)) \Rightarrow$ $[v, w_1] + m$ influences $[v, w_2]$.

METHOD OF GEOMETRICAL RELATIONS

Let T_1 be a sub-tree in T_v, $v \in V(T_1)$. Suppose that we are given an algorithm B (for games B is the choice of the best move) which constructs for any $v \in V(T)$ and any sub-tree $T_1 \subset T_v$ a vertex $w \in N(v)$ such that $\phi_{F, f, T_1}(v) = \phi_{F, f, T_1}(w)$. (Subscript T_1 in ϕ denotes that computation of this ϕ involves edges and vertices only from T_1.) Let us define for T_1 two sub-trees $\delta^{\pm}(T_1)$. $\delta^+(T_1)$ is defined inductively beginning from the root by the conditions $v \in V(\delta^+(T_1))$, $\forall u \in V^{i(v)}(\delta^+(T_1))$ $[N(u, \delta^+(T_1)) = \{B(u, T_1)\}]$, $\forall u \in V^{-i(v)}(\delta^+(T_1))$ $[N(u, \delta^+(T_1)) = N(u, T_1)]$.

Analogously, $\delta^-(T_1)$ is defined inductively by the conditions $v \in V(\delta^-(T_1))$, $\forall u \in V^{i(v)}(\delta^-(T_1))$ $[N(u, \delta^-(T_1)) = N(u, T_1)]$, $\forall u \in V^{-i(v)}$ $(\delta^-(T_1))$ $[N(u, \delta^-(T_1)) = \{B(u, T_1)\}]$. If $T_1 \subset T_v$, $T_2 \subset T_w$, $w \in V^{i(v)}(T_1)$ we set $\epsilon(T_1, T_2) = \tilde{\sigma}(\delta^-(T_1)) \cap \tilde{\sigma}(\delta^+(T_2)) \in \text{Seq } M$.

If T_1, T_2 are sub-trees in T, $P \in \text{Paths } T$, $m \in M$, we say that T_1 influences m (resp. P) if there exists $P_1 \in \text{Paths } \delta^-(T_1)$ such that P_1 influences m (resp. P). We say that T_1 influences T_2 if there exist $P_i \in \text{Paths } \delta^-(T_i)$, $i = 1, 2$, such that P_1 influences P_2. In particular, $T_1 \subset T_v$ influences $[v, w]$, $w \in T_v$, if $\tilde{\sigma}(T_1) \cap \tilde{\sigma}([v, w]) \neq \emptyset$.

Let us now distinguish some special sub-trees. Set $O(v, w) = \sigma(EN(v)) \setminus \sigma(EN(w))$, $L(v, w) = \{m \in \sigma(EN(v)) : [v, w] \text{ influences } m\}$, $v \in T_w$. Sub-tree $T_1 \subset T_w$ is called testing if $\sigma(EN(w, T_1)) \supseteq O(w, v) \cup L(w, v)$ for $w \in V^{i(v)}(T_1)$ and $EN(w, T_1) = EN(w)$ for $w \in V^{-i(v)}(T_1)$. Further, sub-tree $T_2 \subset T_w$, $w \in V^{i(v)}(T_v)$, is called parallel to $T_1 \subset T_v$ if $N(u, T_2) = N(u)$ for $u \in V^{-i(w)}(T_2)$ and $N(u, T_2) = \sigma^{-1}(O(u, w)) \cup N(v + \tilde{\sigma}([w, u]), T_1)$ for $u \in V^{i(w)}(T_2)$. Suppose now that we are given a function $\alpha : M \to R \cup \{+\infty\} \cup \{-\infty\}$. Suppose that $F(e, d) = d$,

$\forall e \in E(T)$, and put $S(v_0) = 0$, $S(v) = \sum_{e \in [v_0, w]} \alpha(\sigma(e))$. Suppose that a condition of majoration holds: $S(v) > S(w) \Rightarrow f(v) > f(w)$ (e.g. for chess $S(v)$ may be taken to be material balance).

Theorem 2. Let $T_1 \subset T_v$, T_1 be a testing sub-tree, $w \in V^{i(v)}(T_v)$. If T_1 does not influence $[v, w]$, $S(w) \leqslant S(v)$ and $v \in V_{BB}(T_1)$ then $w \in V_{BB}(T_2)$ for sub-tree $T_2 \subset T_w$ which is parallel to T_1.

This theorem means, in terms of search, that if at the completion of search over T_1 we have established that $T_1 \subset V_{BB}(T)$ then, in conditions of theorem 2, the search over T_2 is superfluous and T_2 can be cut off.

Let us describe one more result using the notions developed above. Let π be a fixed search computing $\phi_{F,f}(v_0)$. Let $\pi(n, F, f) = u$, $B = A(T(n), F, f)^-$, $e \in EN(u)$. Let us assume, to fix the setting, that $u \in V^+$. Put $K_0 = \emptyset$, $T_0 = T_u$, $G_0 = EN(u)$. Define for each $e \in G_{i-1}$ inductively (for $i = 1, 2, \dots$) a sub-tree $T_{i,e} \subset T_u$ and a set $K_i(u, e)$ in the following manner: $u \in V(T_{i,e})$, $EN(u, T_{i,e}) = e$, $\forall v \in V^-(T_{i,e})$ $EN(v, T_{i,e}) = EN(v)$; $\forall v \in V^+(T_{i,e}) - u$ $[e' \in EN(v, T_{i,e}) \Leftrightarrow \sigma(e') \in \sigma(K_{i-1}(u, e)) \cap \sigma(e') \notin \sigma(EN(u)) \cap (\tilde{\sigma}[u, v])$ influences $\sigma(e')]$; $G_i = \{e' \in G_{i-1} : \phi_{F, f, T_i, e'}(u) \leqslant B\}$, $K_i(u, e) = \{e' \in G_i : T_{i,e} \text{ influences } T_{i,e'}\}$. Set at last $T_e = \lim T_{i,e}$, $G = \lim G_i$.

Theorem 3. Let $G' \subset G$ and π' be a search over sub-tree $T_v \subset T_u$ such that $T_{\pi'}(N, F, f) \cap G' = \emptyset$. Suppose $\tilde{\sigma}([u, v])$ and $T_{\pi'}$ do not influence $T_e \, \forall e \in G'$. If $\phi_{\pi'}(v) = B$ then $\phi_{\pi''}(v) = B$ where π'' is a search such that $E_{\pi''}(T_{\pi''} \cap T_{\pi'}) \setminus E_{\pi'}(T_{\pi''} \cap T_{\pi'}) \subset G'$.

The following method of search reduction is based on theorem 3. Determine for a vertex $u \in V(T)$ the sub-set G. Edges $e \in G$ will not be taken into the search while the current path from u does not influence T_e.

Besides, at the moment of return to a vertex one should check whether $T_{\pi'}$ influences T_e or not. If it does, one should include e into the search. In the contrary case theorem 3 permits one to consider the search from the vertex under consideration as finished. It should be noted that different edges are rejected independently.

REFERENCE

Adelson-Velskiy, G. M., V. L. Arlazarov, A. R. Bitman, A. A. Jivotovskiy & A. V. Uskov (1970) Programming a computer to play chess, (in Russian) in *Uspeckhi Mathem. Nauk 25*, 2(152), 221–60.

A Representation and Some Mechanisms for
a Problem-Solving Chess Program

H. J. Berliner

This paper is a condensation of a recent Ph D dissertation, (Berliner 1974). We describe a program, CAPS-II, and present both its form and some of the results obtained in testing it. The rationale which led us to the design of this program may be found in Berliner (1973). Of necessity, we must omit much of the philosophy behind the program, many of the implementation details, and multiple examples of how it operates. However, we treat in detail what we feel are the major accomplishments of the work.

The domain of the work is chess tactics, and the emphasis is on recognizing situations and dealing with them explicitly. As such, we will be discussing (a) recognition predicates, (b) methods of stating specific problems so that their solution is easier than the general problems that include them, and (c) ways that results of dynamic analysis (tree search) can be made available throughout a search tree for various purposes.

THE RECOGNITION MACHINERY

We first discuss our representation of chess, as it is necessary to understand the remainder of the program. We represent a position as a vector of 1040 words of information. Positions in the variation being currently analyzed are represented as 1040 word segments in a stack which allows analysis to a depth of 20 ply. Within the vector representing a single position there is a hierarchy of complexity of information.

The most primitive elements in this hierarchy of information are the pseudo-legal moves which define the possible transitions from position to position that could be allowable under the rules of chess. Upon this structure is erected the notion of a bearing relationship. This is a relationship of a piece to a square, and in our usage tells under what conditions the piece could pseudo-legally move to that square. The basic bearing relations used in this program are defined below.

DIR(PC,SQ): a piece, PC, bears DIR on square SQ if a king of the opposite color to PC on square SQ would be in check by PC.

OTHRU(PC,SQ): a piece, PC, bears OTHRU on square SQ if PC would be bearing DIR on square SQ, were it not for another (intervening) piece of the same color as PC which has a DIR relation on SQ.

ETHRU(PC,SQ): a piece, PC, bears ETHRU on square SQ if PC would be bearing DIR on square SQ, were it not for one (intervening) piece of the opposite color which has a DIR relation to SQ.

DSC(PC,SQ): a piece, PC, bears DSC on square SQ if PC would be bearing DIR on square SQ, were it not for a piece of its own color that is *not* bearing DIR on SQ.

OBJ(PC,SQ): a piece, PC, bears OBJ on square SQ if PC would be bearing DIR on square SQ, were it not for a piece of the opposite color that is *not* bearing DIR on SQ. Intuitively, this corresponds to a pin ray by the bearing piece through the intervening piece (subject of the pin) and looking for an object to pin it to further down the line.

BLOK(PC1,PC2): a piece, PC1, has a BLOK relation to a sliding piece, PC2, if PC2 would bear DIR on PC1 with all other pieces removed from the board.

BEH(PC,PWN): a piece, PC, has the relation BEH to a pawn, PWN, if it is a rook or a queen and is behind PWN (as it would advance), and bears DIR, or OTHRO, or ETHRU on the square on which PWN is located.

These relations are sufficient to be able to determine whether a piece can: (a) participate in a capture with or without an intervening piece participating; (b) be a pinner of an opposing piece; (c) be the source of a discovered attack if one of its own pieces were to clear the line; (d) be in the path of a sliding piece if all intervening pieces were removed; and (e) help or retard the advance of a pawn.

Once the above information has been gathered, the program embarks on a square-by-square analysis of the board. By using the above relational information it is able to decide which pieces affect the struggle on a certain square. For occupied squares, the safety of each piece is analyzed to be in one of five mutually exclusive categories. These are:

COMPLETELY EN PRISE: the full value of the piece on this square is subject to loss on the opponent's next move.

PARTLY EN PRISE: only part of the value of the piece on this square may be captured with gain, but not the full value of the piece (i.e. a rook attacked by a bishop and defended by a pawn).

BARELY DEFENDED: no capture with gain is possible now, but attacking this square with any one more unit of force will make this piece at least partly *en prise*.

COMPLETELY OVERPROTECTED: the piece is safe against any further single attack by a piece of equal or greater value (i.e. a pawn which is attacked by one pawn and defended by two pawns).

PARTLY OVERPROTECTED: the piece is safe against a set of single attack types, but not safe against the complementary set (i.e. a knight which is attacked by a rook and defended by a king and queen is safe against attacks by queen and king, but not against attacks by any lesser piece).

In the process of making these calculations, the action of pieces of both sides is invoked. Pieces are invoked in reverse order of value, the program also being able to avoid the use of pieces that are known to be pinned, until no more effective piece is available. The computation determines within excellent accuracy limits what the outcome of the struggle on a square will be. During this computation, pieces that are invoked in the safety analysis are assigned functions. By a function we mean a triple (PC, DUTY, SQ). A piece, PC, is said to have DUTY on square SQ if it was invoked for the purpose, D U T Y, during the analysis of square S Q. Typical duties are attacking, defending, over-protecting, and pinning, although blocking and supporting duties also exist in contexts which are discussed later.

Partitioning all pieces into categories that show how readily they are attackable allows a further computation: noting which pieces can be usefully attacked by each class of enemy piece. For instance, it is now possible to determine the set of all pieces that can be usefully attacked by a white queen. This information is in turn used to determine squares where multiple attacks by a certain piece can take place. Other status information has also been gathered about individual pieces. Those that are pinned or considered low in mobility are considered to be worthwhile single targets. Squares where worthwhile attacks can take place are also noted. From the above, it is possible to list the set of all 'attacking' moves for each side. The safety of each attacking move is then determined in the same way as was done for the safety of pieces, and functions are assigned which deal with the execution of the threatened attack and the defence against it. In this way a picture is built up of all the duties of every piece on the board, and this makes it possible to later ascend still further up the ladder of abstraction to find those moves that perturb the existing fabric of the position (as defined by the functions) in interesting ways.

Assigned functions are saved in a cross-referenced format that makes it easy to determine what functions a particular piece has, and what the set of all functions on a particular square are. Squares that contain *en prise* pieces are saved in a vector called B E S T, which keeps track of the threats against material by each side. In computing the above information, C A P S - I I begins to put an interpretation on what is happening on the board.

GOAL STATES

Goal states play a major role in directing the activity of C A P S - I I. They constitute a scheme for partitioning the moves that may be looked at at each node. A goal state defines intuitively a condition and explicitly a set of moves that are appropriate to the problem as perceived by the program. Only these moves may be searched as long as this goal state is in charge. This produces the desired economy of not having to search all moves or all 'attractive' moves, but only those that are deemed pertinent to the problem at hand. This produces a significant reduction in the branching factor of the overall search. A node is always in one and only one of the following goal states.

A G G R E S S I V E: this state consists of discovering and proposing moves that (a) produce double attacks, (b) cause attacks on low mobility pieces, (c) produce discovered attacks, and (d) vacate a square that another piece would like to occupy.

P R E V E N T I V E D E F E N C E: this state is invoked when the side on move finds itself significantly ahead of expectation in material. The state then generates moves that attempt to consolidate the extra material by defending against any apparent threats.

NOMINAL DEFENCE: this state is invoked only when the position is deemed worth defending and no previously tried goal state has produced a good move, nor has a clear enemy threat been noticed in the process. This state defends against apparent threats in the hope that this will satisfy the needs of this node.

DYNAMIC DEFENCE: this state is actuated when a search has backed up to a node with an unsatisfactory value, and the last move tried at this node was blameless. In this case the CAUSALITY FACILITY (see below) is invoked and this state is a part of its operation and is discussed in that context later in this paper.

STRATEGY: this state is invoked only at depths which are specified at the start of the game (and has always been equal to 1 thus far). The strategy implemented here is to call the legal move generator of TECH (Gillogly 1972), which does a positional sort of the legal moves. These are then tried in the given order, with the proviso that moves that were already searched are not searched again. Since this in effect means opening up the search completely, STRATEGY is invoked only at the root of the tree in the current program. This is a very primitive way of looking at strategy. However, the module is completely independent of everything else, and could be replaced incrementally by more sophisticated procedures. Within the present framework, it allows the program to play complete games by making a move selection agency available in situations where no tactical move is preferred.

KING IN CHECK: when the king is in check this state is invoked directly, since the set of legal moves is usually small and can be sorted effectively based upon knowledge of the safety of squares for the pieces.

How the program passes from one goal state to another is discussed below.

MOVE GENERATION

In CAPS-II move generation is very dependent on the recognition machinery. Move generation is done under control of a goal state, which decides the type of move we should be looking for. The following simple move generators are then used to try to find moves that match the description of the desired set of moves.

OCCUPY(SQ) is a move generator that generates all pseudo-legal moves to square SQ for the side on move. One of the uses of OCCUPY is in generating captures.

MOVEAWAY(SQ) is a move generator that generates all pseudo-legal moves for the piece on square SQ. It is useful in defence considerations and for generating discovery moves.

INTERPOSE(SQ1,SQ2): SQ1 and SQ2 define a straight line with SQ1 being the name of the square on which an attacker resides and SQ2 being the square on which a target resides. INTERPOSE finds all intervening squares, and then repeatedly calls on OCCUPY to provide the complete set of interposing moves. Before doing this, INTERPOSE first finds the value of the attacker, and sets a global constant which lets OCCUPY know that moves that counter-attack the attacker along the specified line are to get special heuristic credit.

MOVTOCON(SQ) generates the set of all pseudo-legal moves that bring a piece of the moving side, which at present does not have DIR control on square SQ, into a position where it does; i.e. it brings a new piece to bear on SQ.

MOVE EVALUATION

Moves are then evaluated by the procedure EVALUATE. Our information environment is detailed enough to allow detecting and scoring a proposed tactical move in the environment of the old position, rather than by setting up the new position. This results in a definite saving in computing time. Further, the assignment of functions results in binding certain pieces to certain important duties on the chess board. These duties are considered to be essential if the existing stability of the current position is to be maintained. Therefore, when a move results in perturbing these functions, it is possible to gauge the effect of such a disturbance. Detecting perturbation effects involves noticing whether a piece is moving *en prise*, whether any piece that is set to capture another is committed to other important duties, and whether a moving piece clears or blocks any important squares.

To understand perturbation of a position, it is important to be aware of the various types of moves that can occur and how their merits can be determined. For instance, many programs that use forward pruning of legal moves include all moves that are checks or captures, even if they involve loss of material, just on the chance that some other factors exist which may make such a move successful. Those 'other factors' would, however, have to be discovered at the exponential cost of tree searching. The present program can, because of its refined analytical methods, rule out many checks and captures as completely worthless. This would occur, for instance, when a capture will result in loss of material without causing commensurate 'disturbing effects' on the position. The ability to gauge optimistically such disturbing effects and thus dismiss certain 'sacrificial' moves as having absolutely no sacrificial merit is one of the things that our evaluation procedure is able to deal with effectively.

EVALUATE looks for the main perturbing effects that can occur. These are known in the chess literature as: (a) guard destruction, (b) piece overloading, (c) decoying, (d) line blocking, (e) unblocking and (f) desperados. We discuss each briefly.

Guard destruction occurs when a piece that has a defensive function is captured. Piece overloading occurs when a move is made that requires the exercise of a defensive function by a piece that has another defensive function to fulfill, and cannot fulfill it from the new square. Decoying occurs when a piece has a defensive function, but the exercise of it will bring the piece to a new square. The defending piece is 'decoyed' to this new square, the only necessary condition being that the cost of decoying the piece is not greater than the value of the piece itself. Of course, the ultimate success of the decoy depends on whether it can be successfully attacked at its new location. Line blocking occurs when the action line of an enemy piece with a function is blocked. This can result in either the severing of a defensive tie, or the blocking of an attacking move. Likewise, unblocking occurs when the moving piece makes possible a future attack by one of own pieces either on the square in question or by travelling across the square. Desperados are the sacrificing of men that are already attacked, because an enemy piece of similar value is also attacked and can be expected to be captured immediately after the sacrificed piece is captured. All but the last of these effects depend directly on recognizing the functional bindings that are involved. It should be noted how easy it is to describe the perturbing effects, given the notion of functions, while without this it would be rather difficult.

EVALUATE scores the effect of a proposed move on an existing position. The resulting score is an integer that represents an optimistic view of what the proposed move could accomplish. To facilitate this process, any proposed move gets a quantitative recommendation from the agency that proposes it. The amount of the recommendation is a function only of the effect that the move could have (according to the proposing agency) if it were successful. How much of this value is actually given to the move depends on EVALUATE.

EVALUATE first examines the safety of the new square for the moving piece. If the piece cannot be captured without loss on the destination square, then it gets credit for whatever value its recommending agency gave it. However, if it can be captured advantageously the following procedure is performed: each opposing piece that has been assigned a defensive function on that square has its function list examined to see what other functions it has. The following quantities are then computed:

DEFENSIVE OVERLOAD=maximum [across all squares on which this piece has defensive functions] (the number of material units defended on this square + the value of enemy threats associated with this square).

DECOY VALUE = maximum value (any opposing piece that has a defensive function on this square).

DISTRACT VALUE = maximum [across all opposing pieces that have a defensive function on this square] (value of any *en prise* piece on which this defensive piece has an attacking function).

REDEEMING VALUE = maximum (DEFENSIVE OVERLOAD, DECOY VALUE/2, DISTRACT VALUE/2).

The Redeeming Value is the evaluation for moves that apparently 'don't work', while the evaluation of moves that appear to work is the sum of their recommendation from the proposing agency and the beneficial side effects that they cause.

If a move is selected for searching, two evaluations are developed for the corresponding node in the tree. They are: the nominal value, which counts the material on the board and gives credit to each side for all their material threats as cataloged in BEST; and the pessimistic value (from the point of view of the side that is to move), which counts the material on the board and then adds in only the best capture threat of the side-which-just-moved.

TREE CONTROL

The basic tree search used by CAPS-II is a depth first, mini-maxed search with alpha-beta pruning. This has been supplemented by algorithms which make risk decisions. During the tree search the basic emphasis is on: (a) trying to find properties of the current node which allow termination of the search at that point; (b) making deductions about the current goal state which may lead to abandoning the state or the node; and (c) forward pruning of proposed moves which fail to have certain necessary properties, in order to limit the number of descendants of any parent node.

CAPS-II uses the following level of aspiration scheme. Two limits of aspiration (alpha and beta) are needed in order for each side to know what is the maximum it can hope to achieve at any point in the tree search. An expectation (EXPCT) is needed, that is the best estimate of the value of the position at the root of the tree. Around EXPCT, a margin (MARG) is defined. If a value differs from EXPCT by more than MARG we say it *differs significantly* from EXPCT. If such a value is ever backed up to the root of the tree, EXPCT is changed to that value, and the search is redone.

Alpha and beta are set initially at plus and minus infinity. The value of MARG is set permanently at 68 per cent of the value of a pawn. EXPCT is provided on input of a position and retained from one tree search to the next as the minimaxed value of the last tree search. If a value that is greater than EXPCT plus MARG is ever backed up to the root of the tree, the following occurs: EXPCT is set to the value that has just been backed up, and the new alpha-beta limits become plus infinity and EXPCT minus a very small quantity. The search is repeated unless the value returned is sufficiently high to guarantee a completely winning position for the side making the gain. An algebraically opposite adjustment is made if the value returned to the root of the tree is EXPCT minus MARG.

In order to prevent oscillations in the value of EXPCT, a very conservative view of position evaluation must be taken. This means that wherever there is doubt about the terminal value of a position, the value closest to EXPCT must be chosen. The reason for this is that when the search at a node is terminated as described above, it is almost invariably a non-quiescent value. If such a value should survive all the way to the root of the tree, it will become the new EXPCT for the next tree search. So if the estimate at the terminated node exceeds that which can in reality be achieved from the root node position, the program could well be in a state on the next search in which it cannot fulfill the new EXPCT. This would result in EXPCT being reset to a lower value, and oscillation could result. Therefore, whenever an estimate is made for backing-up purposes, it should be conservative with respect to EXPCT. This means that if a value is significantly greater than EXPCT then only the pessimistic value of this position may be backed up. Likewise, if a value is significantly below EXPCT, the optimistic value of the position must be backed up. Clearly, if the new estimate does not remain significantly different from EXPCT then the conditions for node termination have not been met.

THE CAUSALITY FACILITY

Whenever the search backs up to a node with an unsatisfactory value, the CAUSALITY FACILITY is invoked. The CAUSALITY FACILITY allows determining whether a set of consequences can be definitely dissociated from the last move tried at a node. Only the detection of this condition allows fixing the blame for a set of consequences on something that existed before the search came to this node. Once it is known that the node has inherited a problem, the necessary mechanisms can be set in motion for trying to solve it. Causality is established by comparing a description of a set of consequences (the Refutation Description) with a description of a move. The CAUSALITY FACILITY then decides whether the consequences could have in any way been made possible by the move made. We first describe the data used by the CAUSALITY FACILITY. Then we take up how the CAUSALITY FACILITY gathers this data and uses it for comparisons and decision making.

1. The Refutation Description

During the backup process, whenever a result is acceptable to Alpha-Beta the following data are collected at that node for use by the CAUSALITY FACILITY. These data constitute the Refutation Description. While the simple notation of specifying an origin square and a destination square is enough to describe a move or to play out a game, this is not enough to describe a sequence of moves without having recourse to updating. For the task we are about to describe, we need a description that is rich enough so that properties of a move can be understood without having recourse to updating the board. To do this, we need to know not only the squares of origin and destination, but also the name of the moving piece (since the origin square could at some other time be occupied by a different piece), and the squares which had to be unoccupied in order for the move to be made. These things are essential to a description that can examine a sequence of moves without actually going through the process of setting up the position after each move in the sequence.

RPCS is a bit-vector with bits representing names of pieces. The name bit of the piece that moved to produce this node is set in this vector.

RSQS is a bit-vector with bits representing squares on the board. The bit corresponding to the destination square of the move that produced this node is set in RSQS.

RPATH is a bit-vector with bits representing squares on the board. The bit for any square across which a sliding piece moved in making the made move is set in RPATH. If the move was a non-capture pawn move, then all squares over which it passed including the destination also have bits set for them.

RTGTS is a bit-vector with bits representing names of targets. A comparison is made of BEST for this node with BEST one ply previously. Any squares which are now named as containing material targets, but were not mentioned in the previous BEST, have bits set for the name of the piece on this square to indicate that this threat was created by the last move.

TGTSQS is a bit-vector with bits representing squares on the board. For any RTGTS detected as above, bits are set in TGTSQS for the corresponding squares.

TPATH is a bit-vector with bits representing squares on the board. For any TGTSQS detected as above, if a piece that has an ATTACKING function on this square is a sliding piece, then all the intervening squares have bits set for them in TPATH.

Once this information is generated, it is accumulated during the backing-up process of the tree search. This is done by forming the union of the current description and the previously existing description whenever a node's value is accepted. Thus when returning to a node, a complete description of all that each side has accomplished in the immediate sub-tree and how, is available. If the results of the last move tried at this node were not satisfactory, the CAUSALITY FACILITY consults the Refutation Description in order to decide what can be done about it.

2. The Rationale for the CAUSALITY FACILITY

To understand the value of having a rich representation for this, consider what is possible without it. For instance, assume a sequence of moves resulted in a loss of material. Best current practice would be to remember the first move of the backed-up variation as the 'killer', and then try it first on every move that is served up from here on in the generate and test mode. If the representation was richer and we could get a complete description of all moves in the backed-up variation, then it would be possible to determine the sequence of moves that produced this result. We would then be limited to doing things about this sequence only. This would include such things as suggestions to move or defend any captured piece, capture or pin any capturer, or block the path of any moving piece. However, such a scheme is incomplete since it does not deal with threats that were adequately met.

The present program has a much more complete understanding of a set of consequences. The set of data that the program abstracts from a position and sends back up the tree was discussed earlier. This includes a knowledge of all squares critical to the transportation of pieces that moved, squares on which pieces became targets, and squares over which threats passed. It also includes the names of all pieces that moved or became targets.

When returning to a node, the CAUSALITY FACILITY correlates this description with changes that occurred in the data structure as a result of the move tried at this node. This includes noticing changes in control of critical squares by the losing side, changes in threats as noted in BEST, and whether any unblocking of critical paths occurred as a result of the last move. Making comparisons of these quantities with the refutation description makes it possible to decide whether this move could be to blame for what happened. Whenever this is not the case, the search for a direct method of preventing what happened can begin. For instance, assume a knight was lost as a result of a double attack which also involved the king. Then moving the king away or blocking the threat path to the king are validated as goals for meeting the threat, as well as doing things about the knight and trying to capture the attacking piece or guard the squares on which attacks occurred. The first two goals of this set would not show up in the principal variation, since the major threat is usually avoided. Thus, the present method gets directly at the whole set of consequences, not merely those which were executed in the principal variation.

The CAUSALITY FACILITY does very well at generating defences to deep threats, as is demonstrated below. As a consequence, it is not necessary to make *a priori* decisions about the goodness of certain moves for 'defensive purposes'. Rather, it is possible to wait to see if a defensive problem occurs and then generate the moves that do something about this description. While this is a major advance in the state of the art, it is still considerably short of human performance. First, there are situations in which many defensive moves are suggested, and the program is unable to assign accurate enough values to these moves to prevent a certain amount of hit-or-miss searching. Second, the problem of indirect defences is not treated at all. An indirect defence occurs when a threat is met by playing a move that would allow the execution of a desirable move sequence *only* if the opponent tried to realize his threat. This is quite different from a counter-attack, since the indirect defence is intended to produce its result only when the opponent persists in his attack. A typical indirect defence would involve preparing to move a piece through a square that would be vacated in the process of attempting to execute the threat. The method for detecting indirect defences is to make a null move and then execute the opponent's detected threat sequence. In the final position, the indirect defender now tries to find two moves in succession which would produce a favorable result. One of these moves would then have to be substituted for the null move in order to make the indirect defence work. However, implementing schemes such as this is beyond the scope of the effort reported herein.

GOAL STATE TRANSITIONS

The way the program progresses from goal state to goal state, once having reached a given node, is shown in figure 1. The goal state at each

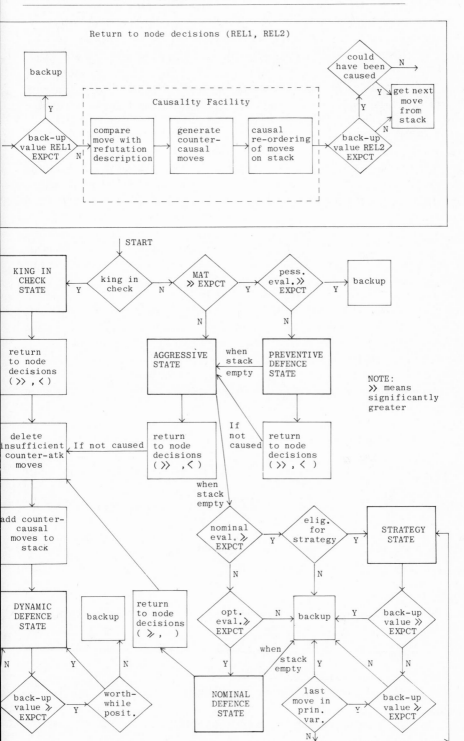

Figure 1. Goal state transition diagram

active node in the tree is remembered in the representation of the node. This means that goal states do not change because of departure and return to a node, but only because of overt decisions made in the course of problem solving at the node. Similarly, the move stack at each node is available for inspection until the node is finally quitted. Thus, any move examined in one goal state will not be tried again if suggested by another.

The 'Return to Node' block at the top of figure 1 shows the decision structure that pertains when returning to a node in most goal states. It is invoked as a sub-routine, with arguments REL 1 and REL 2, by the main transition diagram in the lower part of figure 1. REL 1 is the relation between the backed-up value and EXPCT that when true allows exiting the node immediately. Otherwise, the CAUSALITY FACILITY is invoked. The CAUSALITY FACILITY compares the description of what is best play below this node (the refutation description), with the description of the move made at the node. Based on this comparison, it makes the decision as to whether the consequences could have been caused by the present move. In either case, a list of counter-causal moves is generated. These moves attempt to do something about the refutation description that has been backed up. The exact methods are described below.

REL 2 specifies a relationship between the backed-up value and EXPCT. This relates to whether the backed-up value is satisfactory with respect to the aims of the goal state that the node is currently in. If an unsatisfactory value has been backed up to this node, and the causal analysis reveals that this could not have been caused by the last move tried at this node, it means that a problem has been inherited from higher in the tree. In that case, a transition to a new goal state occurs. If, on the other hand, the result is not deemed to have been caused by the last move or if REL 2 does not obtain, then the program merely does a re-ordering of the untried moves on the move stack, moving those mentioned most often in the counter-causal list to the top of the untried stack. This Causal Re-ordering will result in their being tried earlier, but does not change their value.

Following now the flow chart in the lower part of figure 1, we see that the first determination made is whether the king is in check. If so we go to the KING IN CHECK state in which all legal moves are generated. These are tested in order of decreasing evaluation. If a value significantly greater than EXPCT is ever backed up to this node, the search backs up. If the CAUSALITY FACILITY detects a consequence that could not have been caused by the last move tried, the state is changed to DYNAMIC DEFENCE but the move stack remains intact. If neither of the above occur, causal re-ordering of the untried moves takes place.

If the king is not in check and if the side on move is significantly ahead of EXPCT in material then, if the pessimistic evaluation of this node is also significantly greater than EXPCT, the conditions for backing up have been met. If the latter condition has not been fulfilled, then it means that the opponent still has some important threats (or else the pessimistic evaluation would be better). In this case, the PREVENTIVE

DEFENCE state is entered. Here all moves that move a threatened piece, capture an attacker, block an attacking line, or defend a threatened piece are generated. If this set of moves, when submitted to tree searching, fails to maintain the significantly greater than EXPCT advantage, or if any dynamic problem not caused by the tested move is detected, then the AGGRESSIVE state is entered. This means that the attempt at consolidating the gains has failed, and the program resorts to the more usual method of dealing with a node.

It is possible to get to the AGGRESSIVE state as above, or if the material significantly ahead of EXPCT test fails initially. This means that we know of no reasons at the moment why the side on move should try to make a successful attacking move. As explained earlier, the AGGRESSIVE state is really a set of move generating states. The states are arranged so as to generate moves in order of forcefulness. EVALUATE gives each move a likelihood of success measure. A sorting routine then arranges the moves according to likelihood of success within forcefulness. This results in generating all moves that have aggressive potential (with the exception of moves that only involve an attack on a single non-low-mobility piece, this feature not having been implemented as yet).

After an AGGRESSIVE move has been selected for tree searching, and the search has returned to this node, several things can happen. If the program has found a move that is significantly better than EXPCT, it will back up from this node. If the backed-up value is not significantly better than EXPCT, then the CAUSALITY FACILITY is invoked to do causal analysis and re-ordering of untried moves. If the backed-up value is less than EXPCT, and if the consequences could not have been caused by the last move tried, then the DYNAMIC DEFENCE state is entered. Otherwise, the program selects the next move from the move stack until it exhausts the proposed moves in the AGGRESSIVE state. In that case, if the nominal evaluation of the position is not less than EXPCT, a check is made to see if this node is at a depth that makes it eligible for STRATEGY. If so, this state is entered. Otherwise, the node is exited (i.e. BACKUP). If no successful AGGRESSIVE move was found then if the nominal evaluation of the position were less than EXPCT and the optimistic evaluation greater or equal to EXPCT, then it means that the opponent must have a threat. Since the position has the potential to produce a satisfactory value, the NOMINAL DEFENCE state is entered.

The NOMINAL DEFENCE state is charged with producing defences against statically recognized threats. It is only invoked when no AGGRESSIVE moves have succeeded and the position is considered worthwhile. If in any prior processing of this node a backed-up threat had been recognized, then this state would be by-passed in favor of DYNAMIC DEFENCE. This is very logical, since NOMINAL DEFENCE deals only with statically recognized threats, and one can never be sure that such a 'threat' is really a threat. The move generators of the NOMINAL DEFENCE state produce moves that defend threatened points, move away the pieces on these squares, capture their attackers and block attacking lines. The

NOMINAL DEFENCE state is exited as soon as a move which produces a backed-up value greater or equal to EXPCT is found. If in the process of testing moves, the CAUSALITY FACILITY finds a threat that could not have been caused by the last move tested at this node, then the DYNAMIC DEFENCE state is entered.

The DYNAMIC DEFENCE state is invoked whenever a deep problem has been detected during back up, which was clearly not made possible by the last move tried. The counter-causal moves, which are deemed to be the only ones that can do something about this description, have already been generated by the CAUSALITY FACILITY. Now all moves on the stack that are not mentioned in the counter-causal list, or that do not have a counter-punch at least equal and opposite to the caused value (with respect to EXPCT), are deleted. The remaining counter-causal moves are pushed on to the stack in order of evaluation. These moves are now tested until a value is backed up that is greater or equal to EXPCT. Then if the material plus the best threat of the side to move are not larger than the backed-up value, the node is exited. Otherwise, the search continues until all proposed moves have been tried.

In the present program, the STRATEGY state performs the function of parading all legal moves for testing. It does this only at the root node of the tree (in the current program), and only when the AGGRESSIVE state has failed to produce anything worthwhile. The move generator of the STRATEGY state emphasizes the centralizing and mobilizing effect of each move. It is, in fact, the TECH (Gillogly 1972) move generator which is available to this program as a sub-routine. If a value significantly greater than EXPCT is ever backed up, the node is exited. Otherwise, if the current alpha at the node is greater or equal to EXPCT when the move that is now in the principal variation is proposed, the node is exited. Otherwise, the search continues as long as there are moves to try.

THE CAUSALITY FACILITY AT WORK
1. An Expository Example
Figure 2 shows a position in which black to play has a defensive task. White is threatening mate in two beginning with 1 Q–K8ch. When CAPS-II is presented with this position, it finds no particularly inviting offensive moves since all the black queen checks are adequately guarded and there are no double attack moves. It therefore asks the STRATEGY routine for a move and starts out with 1 ... P–R7.

Play now proceeds 2 Q–K8ch R×Q 3 R×R mate. This result causes the backing up process to begin, and with it the accumulation of the refutation description. Here, we will only follow the process associated with the white moves, since the process associated with the black moves, even though it also goes on, yields no meaningful results in this case. After the moves 1 ... P–R7 2 Q–K8ch R×Q 3 R×R mate, the search begins to back up. When the move 3 R×R mate becomes part of the local principal variation during the backup process, a description of the change in environment that it produced is generated. This description consists of putting the name of the moving rook into RPCS (refutation pieces), putting its destination into RSQS (refutation squares), and putting the squares on its path (K3, K4, K5, K6, and K7) into RPATH. Since the move resulted in a capture, the name of the captured piece is noted in RTGTS (pieces that became target during the refutation). The move resulted in a change in the threat picture in so far as the black king is now attacked when it wasn't one ply earlier. This fact is incorporated by noting the square of the threatened piece (the black king) in TGTSQS, its name in RTGTS, and putting the path squares (KB8) associated with the threat into TPATH. The above entries describe the essential points of interest in the current position and the important changes from the previous one. As the new principal variation continues to survive during backup, this refutation description is backed up too.

Figure 2. Black to play

The first place where this refutation description can be used is one ply further up the tree, at the point where Black played 2 ... R × R. Here, a causal test is performed which shows that the move could have caused the consequences described in the refutation description since it moved to a square mentioned in RSQS. The exact nature of other tests performed as part of the causal test are described later in this example. Since the consequences could have been caused by the last move played, the search at this node continues. But first a set of counter-causal moves are generated, which could be tried in an effort to avoid the consequences anyway. However, here they are useless since there was only one legal move, and that has already been tried.

As backing up continues and the move 2 Q–K8ch becomes part of the new principal variation, a description of it is generated. This consists of putting the name of the queen into RPCS, putting K8 into RSQS, and (since the queen did not cross any squares) putting no path squares into RPATH. The noting of the new threat to the black king (as against the lack of this threat one ply previously) causes its square to go into TGTSQS, its name to go into RTGTS, and the name of the square on the threat path (KB8) goes into TPATH.

When this move is backed up, the union of the new description and the existing refutation description is produced. When the backing up process reaches the point where Black originally played 1 ... P–R7 this description is examined. The following tests are made by the CAUSALITY FACILITY to determine whether the move 1 ... P–R7 could have brought on the consequences described in the refutation description. First a test is performed to see whether the move resulted in moving on to an RSQS square. This is not so. Then a check is made to see whether the name of the moving piece is mentioned in RTGTS (became a later target). This is also not so. Then a check is made to see whether the move vacated a square mentioned in RPATH or TPATH (making a refutation move or threat across this square possible). This, too, is not so. Then each square mentioned in RSQS or TGTSQS is checked in the representation before and after the move 1 ... P–R7 to see if something about the move caused either fewer of own pieces to bear DIR on such a square, or more of the opponent's pieces to bear DIR on such a square. We are interested here both in whether the move resulted in unprotecting such a point, and whether it could have permitted a new enemy piece to bear on the square. Here this involves only K8 and KN8, and no change in the control of those squares occurred. The final test involves noting the pin status of all pieces mentioned in RPCS to see if any such piece was pinned before the made move, and unpinned immediately afterwards. This, too, is not so. Therefore, the conclusion is reached that 1 ... P–R7 could not have caused the consequences, and these must therefore have been inherited from above.

The counter-causal move generator is now invoked in order to generate those moves that can directly counter this description. The counter-causal move generator calls MOVTOCON to generate new moves that can bear DIR on all squares mentioned in RSQS. Here there is only one square (K8) and there is no new way to defend it. Next it calls OCCUPY with the squares of any piece mentioned in RPCS, in order to generate moves that capture pieces involved in the refutation. These pieces are the white queen and rook, and here neither of them are capturable. An additional facility, which is not yet in the program, could impede the movement of such action pieces by trying to pin them against something of greater or equal value to the actual consequences in the principal variation. Next, OCCUPY is called with every square mentioned in RPATH and TPATH, to generate moves which block such paths. This yields Q–K4ch, Q–K5, Q–K6 and R–KB1. Then MOVTOCON is called with the names of squares in TPATH, with the idea that putting a piece in position to occupy such a threat path may defend the threat. Here the only square in TPATH is KB1, and thus the move N–Q2 is generated. Finally, an attempt is made to remove targets by calling MOVEAWAY with the name of any square mentioned in TGTSQS which is occupied by a piece mentioned in RTGTS. This yields the move K–R1. A check is then made to see if any piece mentioned in RTGTS is a low mobility piece that is not presently attacked. Here, the black king qualifies and MOVEAWAY is called with the names of squares that are presently occupied by any king's own piece and to which the king could otherwise have access. However, here neither the KBP nor the KRP can be moved. Thus the counter-causal move generator ends up with suggesting six moves: Q–K4ch, Q–K5,

Q–K6, R–KB1, N–Q2, and K–R1. After a little tree-searching, the program decides that the optimum variation for both sides is: 1 ... Q–K5 2 R × Q P × R. It does not recognize that Black now has a winning position (all of White's threats have been met and there is no effective method to prevent the queening of the black QRP), but it does find this only defence very quickly.

2. Causality Re-ordering

An example of how the program uses causality in order to improve its attacking processes can be seen in figure 3. Here it is Black to play. After spending some time on non-productive issues the program finds the perpetual check: 1 B–R7ch 2 K–R1 B–Q3ch 3 K–N1 with repetition of position. It then raises EXPCT to equality (Black was down in material in the original position), and looks to see if there is something better.

Figure 3. Black to play

The next thing tried is 2 ... B–B2ch 3 K–N1 (here there is no repetition of position and the functional similarity is not discernable to the program), ... B–R7ch and a repetition is again noted. Next the program backs up one ply and tries 3 ... R–R8ch 4 K × R Q–R5ch 5 Q–R3 and decides this position is not good for Black. It then begins to back up, generating a refutation description of all of White's (the refuting side because there was a cut-off) moves. The first point where something can be done about the description is at the point where Black played 2 ... B–B2ch. Here the refutation description is used to generate the set of counter-causal moves. This set is then matched with the moves already on the move stack. Any matching move is promoted to a place higher in the move stack. The move that matches the counter-causal set most frequently is promoted to the highest place. In this case the refutation description mentions the king and queen as RPCS, and mentions the path of the queen in blocking the check in RPATH. Nothing can be done about capturing the king or queen, but among the discovered checks with the bishop that have already been proposed is B–N6ch, which matches a move in the counter-causal set proposed for the purpose of blocking the queen's path. The program then tries 2 ... B–N6ch 3 K–R1 B–R7ch and again finds the repetition of position. Backing up one ply, it tries 3 ... R–R8ch 4 K × R Q–R5ch 5 K–R1 Q–R7 mate. This variation is forced and nothing can be done about it, so the search is exited and the program announces mate in five moves. It should be pointed out that things do not always work out so favorably when causal re-ordering is invoked. If the initial idea tried is unworkable, then moves that help a hopeless cause are promoted. However, by and large, the mechanism helps considerably more than it hinders.

TESTS ON THE PROGRAM

CAPS-II was tested on many middle-game chess tactics problems from standard textbooks on chess. We also had it play a few complete games of chess. In both these modes it ran with a maximum depth of ten ply. CAPS-II did not do too well in the games, since it has little positional knowledge, and more importantly the tactics mechanisms that it has are still not complete, causing it to make occasional blunders that would wipe out whatever good it had achieved earlier. However, it did quite well on the tactics problems as reported below.

It is interesting to note that the branching factor (average number of successors to a node) of the trees grown while solving textbook problems is 1.5, while the branching factor for games is about 3.0. The curve for the expected number of successors for a node is in the form of an exponential decay in both cases. Approximately 70 per cent of all nodes have zero or one successor. This compares extremely well with standard programs which have a branching factor of about 5 to 6. Since the program does not as yet play as well as these, nor treat positional issues, some caution should be exercised in evaluating this fact. However, from our experience in developing the program, we do feel that branching factors of this low order can be maintained by continuing the building process in the same vein as that which has been reported here. The reason that the branching factor is higher for games than for problems appears to be that the activity in problems is better focussed. If the program is able to follow this focus it solves the problem in a reasonably effective manner; if not, it usually does not find too much to waste its time on. In games, the situation is frequently not so clear, and the program spends more time in exploring non-productive issues.

CAPS-II was presented with the first 200 problems from Reinfeld (1958), a book that teaches chess tactics by examples. Since these problems were also presented to the program TECH and a Class A player there were good comparative data available for evaluating CAPS-II's performance. For all three performers the performance criterion was that the problem had to be solved in five minutes of (CPU) time to be counted correct. For the programs, supporting output was required to show that the correct answer was not selected spuriously. Depth is defined as the depth of the deepest non-capture in any branch of the principal variation. This definition is being used mainly because of the structure of TECH, in which all capture sequences are examined as part of the quiescence process. Thus if a principal variation ends with one or more captures, these would be included as part of the quiescence analysis if the search went to the depth of the previous non-capture move in that variation. This is not an unreasonable definition of depth, since in most positions there exist sequences of captures which either do not disturb the status quo or reap the fruits of the previous moves. Both these situations can be considered to be 'self-evident' extrapolations of the current position, i.e. not related to any additional depth of search.

Table 1.

depth	both right	TECH only	CAPS-II only	both wrong	total
1	1	1	0	0	2
2	6	4	0	0	10
3	24	7	0	2	33
4	23	16	1	2	42
5	1	3	13	11	28
6	0	0	11	20	31
7	0	0	5	10	15
8	0	0	1	9	10
9	0	0	6	3	9
10	0	0	1	4	5
>10	0	0	0	11	11
total*	55	31	38	72	196

*These totals do not sum to 200, because problems on which partial credit was given are not included.

Table 1 shows the performance of TECH versus CAPS-II on individual problems as a function of the depth of the principal variation. The interesting thing about this table is the very pronounced skewing of results as a function of depth. Because of its exhaustive search TECH does not miss any problems of depth 1 or 2. Then as the amount of work increases the probability of TECH failing to solve a problem goes up steadily, until it can no longer solve any problems of depth 6 or greater in the five minutes allowed. On the other hand, CAPS-II misses a certain number of problems, at every depth. The percentage increases slightly as a function of depth, but the most important point to note is that CAPS-II, because of its approach, is able to solve some problems at every depth because the exponential explosion does not hurt it as much as a more conventionally designed program. It is reasonable to assume that as its perceptual facilities improve, CAPS will continue to increase the percentage it solves correctly at any depth. The conclusions associated with this table are probably the most important ones in this paper.

It is interesting to contrast the results of CAPS-II versus TECH with a comparison of CAPS-II versus the Class A player as shown in table 2. Here the Class A human player very clearly excels the program in every category. This is, in our judgement, indicative of his greater understanding and flexibility of approach. However, the Class A player does not completely dominate CAPS-II's performance.

This can be seen in table 3 which shows the comparative performance of the two on individual problems. Again the Class A player has the far superior performance. However, the next to last column shows that there were quite a few instances where CAPS-II was able to solve problems that the Class A player did not solve. This, in any case, serves to encourage us into believing that the basic approach has considerable potential, and will allow producing ever better programs as more and more of the details of tactical perception and analysis are built in.

Table 2.

depth	total	% right/CAPS-II	% right/Class A
1	3	50	100
2	10	60	90
3	33	73	91
4	42	57	79
5	29	50	69
6	31	35	61
7	15	33	67
8	11	13	73
9	10	60	70
10	5	20	40
>10	11	0	18

An interesting test, which helps to reveal some of CAPS-II's perceptual ability, was performed on a sequence of fourteen positions, all of which were short mates. These positions had been selected because they could be solved rapidly, and the time to solution varied inversely with the playing strength of human players who had solved them earlier. Using standard settings, CAPS-II solved five of the fourteen positions correctly in five seconds or less. This appears to speak highly for CAPS-II's ability to diagnose and carry out simple attacks on the king. This in turn is due to the perceptual processing that the program engages in, which does a very good job of noticing powerful attacking moves. On the problem that was the single greatest discriminator of playing strength, CAPS-II achieved the highest possible rating, a grandmaster rating, by solving the

Table 3.

depth	both right	Class A only	CAPS-II only	both wrong
1	1	1	0	0
2	6	3	0	1
3	21	9	3	0
4	20	13	4	5
5	8	12	6	2
6	6	13	5	7
7	2	8	3	2
8	1	6	0	3
9	5	2	1	2
10	0	2	1	3
>10	0	2	0	8

problem in five seconds. Significantly, in solving this problem, the program made a wrong start on the correct idea, used the CAUSALITY FACILITY to find the correct implementation of the idea, raised the level of aspiration as an intermediate gain of a pawn was found, and deepened the solution to find the mate in three moves (all in five seconds).

Figure 4. White to play

Figure 5. Black to play

The most difficult problem that CAPS-II has ever solved is shown in figure 4. This is a famous combination stretching a full five moves for each side from the text position. The program looked at many possibilities, generating a tree of 897 nodes, but delivered the correct principal variation, letter-perfect as it is in the book. An investigation of the analysis tree showed it also correctly diagnosed all sub-variations. The correct moves and essential sub-variations are: 1 N×P! P×N Q×KPch K–R1 3 Q–K7! Q–N1 4 R×Pch! Q×R 5 Q×Rch winning; or 2 ... K–B1 3 Q–Q6ch, followed by Q×R; or 2 ... K–N2 3 Q–K7ch, followed by Q×R.

Another fine achievement was the solution of the problem in figure 5. This is a famous opening trap, the correct move for Black being 1 ... Q×N because, after 2 B×Q, B–N5ch wins. It took the program twelve CPU seconds and 49 nodes to discover the inadequacy of 1 ... P×N (because of 2 Q×Qch ... 3 B×Pch and 4 B×R) and then find the correct solution. Most of the credit for this must go to the CAUSALITY FACILITY, which quickly pinpointed the cause of the loss after 1 ... P×B and, failing to find any meaningful alternatives at greater depth, returned the search to the top where the correct move was tried next and found to be good.

FUTURE CONSIDERATIONS
The following directions appear to be the most appropriate continuations of the research reported herein, and we are now engaged in developing these.

Complete Causality
The CAUSALITY FACILITY as it is presently constituted is only able to dissociate the blame for a set of consequences from the move made at the root of the sub-tree for which the consequences were collected. This means in effect that it can detect a 'threat' that the move in question failed to meet and also did not cause. However, it is also important to be able

to determine whether a move brought on a set of consequences that would not have been possible otherwise. This is the case of a move being 'bad', and the refutation description gives the reason it is bad. To detect this case the following procedure is required.

. When the CAUSALITY FACILITY cannot dissociate a set of consequences from a move, a null move is executed in place of the suspect move. Then the program tries to execute the Consequence Description in the sub-tree below this node. If the consequence description can be executed to produce a success value, then the suspect move was clearly not responsible. If the consequence description cannot be executed or a success value is not achievable, then the suspect move clearly was responsible. The ability to make this decision correctly leads us directly to the next subject.

The Positing of Lemmas
There are certain invariants that tend to exist on the chess board from move to move. For instance, a certain check with the queen may continue to be bad because the checking square is adequately guarded. In their static analyses, programs manage to diagnose a high percentage of such cases correctly. However, because the static analysis will make some errors or interpret some unclear situation liberally (as it must), there will be some moves proposed which turn out to be bad. Further, since the static analysis always works in the same way (e.g. it does not learn), it will continue to propose these 'bad' moves in similar board positions, and each time such a move is searched it will generate a sub-tree which in retrospect constitutes wasteful activity.

The first step toward preventing this activity is to detect that a particular move was in fact bad. This is what the completion of the CAUSALITY FACILITY offers. Once such a move has been detected, the essential environment in which its badness was detected must be specified. This consists of knowing the squares, pieces, and paths specified by the consequence description, and where each mentioned piece is in the position in which the bad move was made. It is now possible to posit a Lemma—this being knowledge that a certain move will be bad as long as the described environment does not change. With this knowledge, any proposed move may be looked up in the lemma file and, if it has been previously cataloged, the program may determine if the current position contains any essential changes from the lemma environment which might make the move succeed. It is important to note that should it be decided to try the move, and should it again fail, that it would now be possible to generalize the lemma to include the union of the two environments, thus making it stronger. In a somewhat similar way, it is possible to generalize about the movements of a single piece, if more than one lemma exists with respect to its moves.

Lest all this seem too beautiful and easy, we should point out that this implementation of lemmas leaves out some conditions under which a bad move may become good. These conditions pertain to such things as pieces, which are presently defended and do not show up in the refutation description, becoming undefended and then becoming targets that would interfere with the successful execution of the refutation. Other possibilities also exist, but this subject is beyond the scope of the present paper.

Themes

It is possible that the concept of goal states is not stringent enough to produce branching factors of the order of 1.5 or less in ordinary chess positions. The notion of lemmas will help achieve this goal; however further help is possible. When a move is selected for searching, it is because it was recommended by a goal state and approved by EVALUATE. Once the searching of the sub-tree below this move begins in CAPS-II, this information is no longer used. It seems clear that making available to its sub-tree the reasons why a move was selected for searching will improve the utility of continuation moves that are to be searched. For instance, if a move was selected because it cleared a square for another piece, it seems reasonable that only moves that follow up on this clearance and otherwise new, outstanding moves should be considered. It is possible for each reason that a move was generated, and for each redeeming feature that was noticed in EVALUATE, to provide a set of criteria for follow-up moves. These criteria should then be pushed down the tree, the union of the current set and the previously existing set being formed each time a move is selected for searching. While the set of meaningful follow-ups is an arbitrary notion, which can be expanded as a program matures, it is clear that this dissemination of information away from the root of a sub-tree will provide helpful guidance to a goal oriented problem solving mechanism.

ACKNOWLEDGEMENT

This work was supported by the Advanced Research Projects Agency of the Office of the Secretary of Defense (Contract F44620-73-C-0074) and is monitored by the Air Force Office of Scientific Research.

REFERENCES

Berliner, H.J. (1973) Some necessary conditions for a master chess program, in *Proc. 3rd Int. Joint Conf. on Artificial Intelligence*, 77–85. Stanford Research Institute Publications Dept.

Berliner, H.J. (1974) Chess as problem solving: the development of a tactics analyzer. PhD dissertation, Computer Science Department, Carnegie-Mellon University, Pittsburgh, Pa.

Gillogly, J.J. (1972) The Technology chess program. *Artificial Intelligence* 3, 145–63.

Reinfeld, F. (1958) *Win at Chess*. Dover Books.

King and Rook Against King: Historical Background and a Problem on the Infinite Board

D. Michie

Mechanizations of this elementary end-game (KRK) have been done by Torres y Quevedo in the late 19th century, by B. Huberman (1968), by C. Zuidema (1974) and by M. Bramer (1975). These implementations are reviewed in the light of a distinction between 'procedural' and 'structural' approaches to embedding domain-specific knowledge.

A structural approach is described, which differs from previous KRK exercises in that it aims at a minimal-path, as opposed to a merely 'reasonable', strategy. In this paper results are reported for a problem on the infinite board.

INTRODUCTION

Machine Intelligence is concerned with programming computers for complex problem-domains, i.e. domains for which solution algorithms are known, yet are doomed by the combinatorial explosion to lose on the clock. Computer chess is a classic example. A well-known approach, first proposed in 1912 by Zermelo, is based on the idea of looking ahead along all possible paths to the end of the game. Unaided, this algorithm lacks practical applicability. Discussing it in his celebrated essay of 1950, Claude Shannon pointed out that 'a machine operating at the rate of one variation per micro-microsecond would require over 10^{90} years to calculate its first move!'

Note the qualification 'unaided'. The development of a system of artificial aids whereby domain-specific knowledge—theorems, facts, tricks, statistics, goals, evaluations and the like—can be brought to the aid of such algorithms is the defining pre-occupation of the discipline called AI by its practitioners. But we must not lose sight here of what is general and what is specific, for the situation is quite intricate. AI seeks *general* methods of bringing *domain-specific* aids to the assistance of *general* algorithms. Thus the search algorithm to which Shannon was referring is a rather general one, of equal validity for Chess, Checkers, Go, Go-moku, Kalah, Nim, Tic-tac-toe and so forth, i.e. for any two-person zero-sum game of perfect information without chance moves. But the knowledge that permits a Grandmaster to obtain, almost without error, the same results as Shannon's 10^{90}-year computation is *specific to chess*. Indeed, the part of such knowledge that has already been codified occupies a considerable volume of print in the chess libraries of the world. According to the position maintained here, AI is the science of discovering *general* mechanisms whereby *specialised* knowledge can be made to steer *general* search algorithms, so that (against all the odds) they perform efficiently in specialised domains.

FORMS OF KNOWLEDGE

A gradation of forms can be recognised.

1. *Rote-memory of specific instances.* Samuel's (1959) checkers-playing program used a 'dictionary tape' to store previously encountered board positions with their computed 'backed-up' evaluation scores. Since the computation of scores involved large lookahead trees great savings were attained, together with an increase in the effective depth of lookahead. Chess has a space of some 10^{45} legal positions as contrasted with about 10^{15} for checkers, so that the benefits to be obtained from rote-knowledge are in chess limited mainly to the storage of 'book openings'.

2. *'Type' positions or patterns.* An example from Zuidema is reproduced in figure 1. Pattern-knowledge constitutes the greater part of the chess Master's skill—overwhelmingly so in lightning chess, which does not allow time to pursue long trains of explicit reasoning.

Figure 1. Two instances of a pattern that suggests a standard mating sequence starting with a bishop sacrifice: 1 B × Pch K × B 2 N-N5ch K-N1 3 Q–R5, threatening mate on R7. In the left-hand instance the suggestion is sound, in the right-hand unsound. Zuidema (1974), from whom the example is taken, points out that pattern-knowledge has in general to be checked on each occasion by detailed lookahead.

3. *Theorems.* An elementary example of the use of this form of knowledge is provided by the theorem that says: if in a given position a knight is the only piece free to move, he can prevent the enemy king from alternating between two opposite-coloured squares if and only if his square is opposite-coloured to that of the king. This follows from the fact that the knight's move always changes the colour of the square on which he stands. An illustration is given in figure 2, adapted from a study published in 1860 by Sam Lloyd. Black threatens to queen after N–N7ch. So White plays 1 B–R1. Because of the above theorem Black must not now capture the bishop for, after 1 ... K × B, White's king bottles up the enemy king by 2 K–B2 (if he goes to B1, opposite in colour to the black knight's square, then we will have 2 ... N–B4, 3 K–B2 N–N6, and Black takes the stopper out of the bottle). So instead of capturing, Black plays 1 ... N–N7 ch, 2 K–Q2 K × B. Using the same theorem, White places his king on B1, a square of the same colour as the enemy knight. Wherever the knight now

roams, he will always return with the wrong parity, and White has the black king permanently shut in.

Figure 2. White to play and draw (study no. 49 from Bán 1963). The solution involves use of an elementary chess theorem (see text).

In this paper we shall not concern ourselves with this highest level of abstraction but with what can conveniently be represented in the form of *patterns*. But we should bear in mind that one way in which a pattern can get into memory is by abstraction from sample positions to which a theorem has been successfully applied. The expert eventually recognises positions of the same *type* as figure 2, abstracting from numerous episodes of reasoning. But once the pattern is there, explicit reasoning is required only for checking. In domains as tractable as the one to be considered it may not be required at all.

How To Get the Knowledge In

There are two views about where domain-specific knowledge should be put. One says 'in data-structures', and the other says 'in procedures'.

According to the first approach we retain the solution algorithm more or less in its pure form, and have it communicate at arm's length with a domain-specific knowledge-base from which relevance-matching routines dig out 'advice' for the algorithm at appropriate moments. If on the other hand we follow the procedural approach we rebuild entirely the original naive algorithm, intimately 'embedding' domain-specific knowledge into the constituent procedures of the rebuilt program. Devotees of the first approach say that the second gives you a fast-running but inflexible program, hard to read, understand, document or revise, and almost impossible to endow with powers of self-modification. Devotees of the second approach say that the first will only become worth discussing when 'advice programming' has been successfully applied to at least one non-trivial problem.

There is of course no compulsion to make a cult of either the one or the other approach. Blends are possible, yet the distinction remains important. The breeding of mules, which have their own uses independent of the arts of horsemanship and the needs of donkey-work, does not nullify the labour of taxonomists. This paper re-examines a well-worn problem in chess programming with an eye to the distinction between the two approaches. After a review of earlier mechanizations of the ending king and rook against king (KRK), a problem of J. Bán for the infinite board is solved. The solution is used as an introduction to the 'structural' approach to knowledge-representation.

EARLIER MECHANIZATIONS OF KRK
Torres' Machine

In the last decade of the 19th century Torres y Quevedo designed and built an electro-mechanical device to play the KRK game. The machine had to achieve checkmate from any starting position subject to a qualification to be explained later. KRK is one of the easiest of the standard mates, yet it is not trivial to define an adequate strategy let alone implement it in electrical circuitry. So Torres' achievement must be ranked as a *tour de force*. The machine must also have been exceptionally durable, for Pierre de Latil reproduces a photograph of Torres' son demonstrating its operation to Norbert Wiener at the 1951 Cybernetic Congress in Paris.

Torres did not publish, but the general plan of the machine has been described by Vigneron (1914). By making common-sense interpretations in places where his text is unspecific or obscure it is possible to arrive at a reconstruction. This is shown in table 1 in the form of six decision rules, checked by program as described in the Appendix. The reconstruction implies a limitation not mentioned by Vigneron, namely that the initial state of the game requires to be set up so that the white rook already stands in one of the two 'zones' (see table 1) and 'divides' the two kings with rank(BK) < rank(WR) < rank(WK). I have learned from Mr Alex Bell that a Torres-based machine that he saw operating in Madrid in 1958 conformed essentially to this precondition. Moreover, experiment with the strategy shows that for the worst-case starting position, shown in figure 3, checkmate requires 62 moves. Nemes (1969) cites the same figure. The cumulative weight of these separate items of confirmation leaves little doubt that table 1 represents a correct reconstruction.

The strategy shown introduces some of the main concepts of the KRK game, and demonstrates how few are needed if the aim is merely to arrive at checkmate, irrespective of the length of the path. Fine's (1941) conjecture that with White to move mate can be guaranteed in at most seventeen moves (33 ply) has been replaced by the definitive result 31 ply, obtained by exhaustive enumeration (Clarke, this volume). Compare with Torres' 123-plus (the 'plus' standing for additional moves concerned with establishing the precondition). The multiplication and refinement of concepts for progression from a Torres-like strategy to an optimal-path strategy (defined under the minimax condition that White always plays to hasten the end and Black to delay it) is a matter of some interest.

In table 1 Torres' eight conditions are separated by horizontal lines into four groups corresponding to four broad strategic concerns.

First group: is the rook actually or potentially in danger? If so, then the rook should flee, says rule 1.

Second group: does the rook 'confine' the black king, i.e. bar him

Table 1. Reconstruction, in the form of six decision rules, of Torres' KRK machine. Ranks are assumed to be numbered downwards from the top of the board, where checkmate is finally delivered.

PRECONDITION: divides (WR, WK, BK) and (file(WR) $\leq$ 3 or file(WR) $\geq$ 6)	1	2	3	4	5	6
CONDITIONS			RULES			
1. samezone(BK, WR)	Y	N	N	N	N	N
2. rank(WR) $-$ rank(BK) $>$ 1	—	Y	N	N	N	N
3. rank(WR) $-$ rank(BK) $=$ 1	—	—	Y	Y	Y	Y
4. rank(WK) $-$ rank(BK) $>$ 2	—	—	Y	N	N	N
5. rank(WK) $-$ rank(BK) $=$ 2	—	—	—	Y	Y	Y
6. file(BK) $-$ file(WK) $=$ 0	—	—	—	Y	N	N
7. file(BK) $-$ file(WK) is *odd*	—	—	—	—	Y	N
8. file(BK) $-$ file(WK) is *even* and *non-zero*	—	—	—	—	—	Y
ACTIONS						
1. WR flees horizontally from BK	X	—	—	—	—	—
2. WR advances vertically one rank	—	X	—	X	—	—
3. WK advances vertically one rank	—	—	X	—	—	—
4. WR moves horizontally one file	—	—	—	—	X	—
5. WK moves horizontally towards BK	—	—	—	—	—	X

Comments

Condition 1: 'samezone' is defined in terms of two 'zones', consisting of the files 1-3 and the files 6-8 respectively, i.e. file(BK) $\leq$ 3 *and* file(WR) $\leq$ 3 *or* file(BK) $\geq$ 6 *and* file(WR) $\geq$ 6 (leaving holes in the strategy from some starting positions—easily filled if we were to depart from Vigneron).

Condition 6: the 'direct opposition': a check from WR can force BK to yield a rank.

Condition 8: the 'distant opposition': the aim now is to convert it by a series of king moves into the direct opposition (or have the BK yield a rank before he is forced to).

Action 1: 'flees horizontally' means 'moves so as to maximise the file distance between BK and WR'. Vigneron is not specific.

Action 2: as part of Rule 2 this effects a step-by-step advance until WR 'confines' BK (i.e. until Condition 3 becomes true). In Rule 4 the same Action gives check in response to Condition 6.

Action 3: 'vertically' is an assumption. Vigneron is not specific.

Action 4: a 'waiting move' to change the parity of the inter-king file distance. When a choice exists, prefer the move away from BK.

from retreating one rank? If not, keep advancing the rook, says rule 2.

Third group: is the inter-king rank distance small enough to begin manoeuvring for the 'opposition'? If not, then keep advancing the white king, says rule 3.

Fourth group: does the white king possess the direct opposition? If so, then exploit it with check, says rule 4. If not, then perhaps the distant opposition? Then try for the direct opposition, says rule 6. Otherwise rule 5 prescribes a waiting move.

The simplicity of Torres' decision logic underlies both (a) the extra-ordinary compactness with which the algorithm can be represented (logical redundancy among the conditions allows us to delete three rows

1	R-K2	(5)	K-B6	12	R-N3ch	(4)	K-N5
2	K-N1	(6)	K-Q6	13	K-N2	(3)	K-B5
3	R-KR2	(1)	K-B6	14	R-QR3	(5)	K-K5
4	R-KN2	(5)	K-Q6	15	K-B2	(6)	K-Q5
5	K-B1	(6)	K-K6	16	K-K2	(6)	K-B5
6	K-Q1	(6)	K-B6	17	R-KR3	(1)	K-Q5
7	R-QR2	(1)	K-K6	18	R-KN3	(5)	K-B5
8	R-QN2	(5)	K-B6	19	K-K2	(6)	K-N5
9	K-K1	(6)	K-N6	20	K-B2	(6)	K-R5
10	K-B1	(6)	K-R6	21	K-N2	(6)	K-N5
11	K-N1	(6)	K-N6	22	R-N4ch	(4)	K-N4
					etc.		

The sequence-pattern exhibited by moves 13-22 is repeated four more times; adding the first twelve moves, we have 5 x 10 + 12 = 62.

Figure 3. An adverse initial position for the Torres strategy, requiring 62 moves by White to force checkmate. The move sequence is given underneath the diagrammed board position; numbers in parentheses identify rules from table 1.

from the upper part of table 1 if we wish) and (b) the extraordinary in-elegance of its play. Subsequent mechanisers have achieved gains under heading (b) at the expense of losses under heading (a). One of them, Coen Zuidema, an International Chess Master and computer scientist, remarks: 'A small improvement entails a great deal of effort.' We now turn to his study of K R K.

Zuidema's Program

It is a normal approach to any tricky problem, in AI as elsewhere, to start with a crude, rough-hewn, Torres-like strategy and then to improve it piece-meal by repeated cycles of testing and patching, as in the de-bugging of computer programs (see Sussman 1974). But note in passing that debugging is ordinarily directed towards a correct implementation of a *given* strategy rather than towards the strategy itself.

Optimizing a strategy by trial and error hinges critically on the detection of exceptions. It would be tempting for example to introduce into table 1 a refinement of rule 1 to detect in the initial position the protection of the rook by the white king as a substitute for fleeing.

Zuidema's (1974) study describes two A L G O L 60 programs for

KRK. The second represents an elaboration designed to correct some of the inelegancies of play exhibited by the first. As worst-case behaviour the primitive version required twenty-seven moves (53 ply) to mate from one particular position (Zuidema's figure 29) for which the length of the minimax path is known from Clarke's work (this volume) to be fourteen moves (27 ply).*

The improvement of play in the second version (the ALGOL text of which is given in full) is not easy to assess from Zuidema's account. For him, however, it was evidently purchased at too high a price: 'The conclusion forces itself that refining the algorithm and exceptions of rules give rise to an overburdened program, . . .' and in his Introduction: 'A more refined strategy is needed to elevate level of play. A small improvement, however, entails a great deal of expense in programming effort and program length. The new rules will have their exceptions too.'

Table 2 gives the total bulk, in 60-bit words, of compiled code for Zuidema's old and new versions. The procedure 'room' described below contains nearly all the domain-specific knowledge.

Table 2. Program length, and some of its components, in C. Zuidema's old and new versions (units are 60-bit words of object code).

	old	new
total program	2000	2900
input-output	715	715
the procedure 'room'	280	1070

Torres' strategy does not look ahead, but selects its moves directly on the basis of the current position. By contrast, Zuidema's does not prune the number of possible moves down to only one, but applies some milder preliminary criteria to produce a candidate set. Pruning is at three levels:

1. *Unconditional.* Example: rook moves to ranks 2, 3 and 4 and to files 2 and 3 are excluded: the program transposes every position so that the black king stays in the triangle e5–e8–h8 (algebraic notation). The move to rank 1 is not excluded so that it can be used as a 'waiting move' when required. The fact that waiting moves *are* required in KRK should be noted. If Black is allowed null moves then White cannot force the win.

2. *Conditional on features of the current position.* Example: if the inter-king rank distance is more than three, then a king move is always played unless the rook is *en prise*.

3. *Conditional on features of the successor position.* Example: a king move which would enlarge the inter-king rank distance is excluded.

The candidate moves that pass this three-level filter are then applied to generate a set of successor positions, and these are scored by a purely static evaluation function (i.e. no further lookahead is employed in calculating it). This function is computed by the procedure 'room' based,

*White's first error was his third move, Rg4. Kd1 was necessary.

with many elaborations and refinements, on counting the number of squares over which the black king would be free to roam if the white pieces sat still. The concept is an advance on those of Torres and leads to more purposeful 'hemming in' of the enemy. The 'room' idea is also of general chess utility beyond the bounds of KRK.

Huberman's Program

In 1968 Barbara Huberman wrote a program to play the endings king and rook against king, king and two bishops against king, and king, bishop and knight against king.

Confining attention to the first of these, play was respectable, although not quite as economical as Zuidema's new version. The principles on which it was constructed were totally different, and are of interest in exemplifying in pure form what we have termed the 'structural' approach. Huberman's base of domain-specific knowledge was a set of logic formulae expressing 'goals'. The domain-independent solution algorithm took the form of a procedure for constructing a 'forcing tree' from which playing sequences satisfying the goals could be generated. Huberman's study provided a convincing demonstration of the versatility achievable by the structural approach: the same program with a different assertion-base coped successfully with the formidable ending K + B + N against K.

Bramer's Program

Recently M. A. Bramer (1975) has reported an experiment with the KRK endgame. His approach has features in common with Huberman's, but the salient differences are: (a) Bramer's definition and ordering of goal patterns (he calls them 'equivalence classes') is such that no search at all is required, the principle of play being simply 'in any position, choose the move which gives the most favourable successor position'. (b) The quality of play is much better. Bramer states that 'no case has so far been found where the program takes more than the theoretical maximum necessary number of 17 moves before checkmate . . .'. Since we know from Clarke (this volume) that the theoretical maximum is in fact sixteen, we can infer that Bramer's program generates sub-optimal play, while accepting his assurance that it is at least near-optimal.

CURRENT WORK

Optimal KRK

In the restricted KRK context Huberman's work represents the use of a steam-hammer to crack a nut. Accordingly we consider the question: can we design a nut-sized hammer on similar principles and use it to do what Huberman did not do (because she did not attempt it), namely to build an *optimal* KRK strategy in the minimax sense defined earlier. We shall require the program modules and data elements to be few and simple. We shall also require the process of building and re-building the strategy ('programming effort' in Zuidema's terms) to be straightforward and not burdensome.

In a step-wise approach to the final program, a version was developed for the problem of mating the lone king on an infinite board with one corner.

The Infinite Board
On a board which extends without limit in all directions the black king cannot be mated even if he co-operates. This follows from the fact that in a checkmate position every square of the 3×3 array shown in figure 4 must be attacked by white pieces. The white king can attack at most three squares adjacent to the enemy king and the white rook can attack at most three more. We are left with a deficit of three squares.

Figure 4. The black king cannot be in checkmate from WK and WR on an infinite edge-less board. All nine squares shown above must be controlled, exceeding the combined powers of the two attacking pieces.

On an infinite board with a single edge (or with two parallel edges) the mate can only be forced from a few special starting positions: in the general case the black king can be brought to checkmate only if he co-operates. The presence of at least one corner is thus a necessary condition for mate to be forceable regardless of starting position. The reasons are not immediately obvious. An outline proof follows which introduces notations and methods basic to the rest of this study. We later show the condition to be sufficient as well as necessary.

The left-hand diagram of figure 5 shows the sole checkmate pattern possible on the infinite board with edge but no corners. The uniqueness of the checkmate pattern follows from the fact that the edge abolishes three of the nine squares of figure 4 and the WK and WR each deploys his maximum competence in taking care of three each of the six remaining. No other arrangement of pieces allows this.

Proof that legal starting positions exist from which White cannot force checkmate in any sequence of steps proceeds by noting that all forcing sequences terminate in pattern 0 (left-most in figure 5). Hence they can all be systematically generated by building a derivation tree backwards from pattern 0, first by constructing all patterns from which a white-optimal move leads in a single step to pattern 0, then by constructing all the patterns from which a black-optimal move leads in a single step to one or another of the level-1 patterns already generated,

Figure 5. Tree of optimal derivations of the checkmate pattern for infinite cornerless KRK. The board is bounded to the north by a single edge.

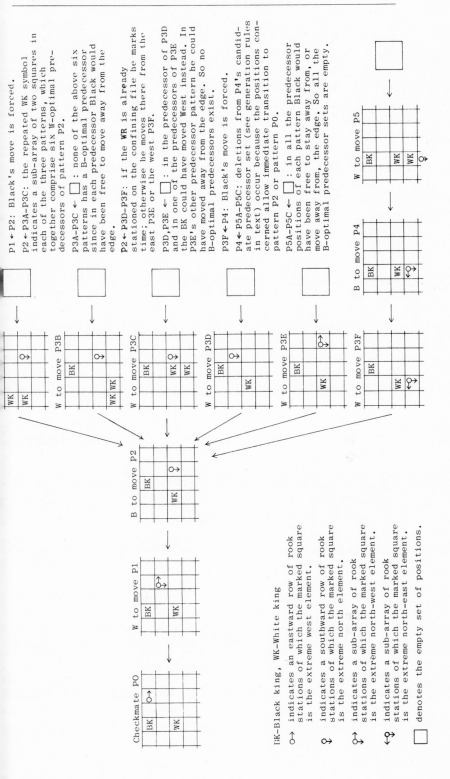

P1←P2: Black's move is forced.

P2←P3A-P3C: the repeated WK symbol indicates a sub-array of two squares in each of the three patterns, which together comprise six W-optimal predecessors of pattern P2.

P3A-P3C ← □ : none of the above six patterns has a B-optimal predecessor since in each predecessor Black would have been free to move away from the edge.

P2←P3D-P3F: if the **WR** is already stationed on the confining file he marks time; otherwise he moves there from the east P3E or the west P3F.

P3D,P3E ← □ : in the predecessor of P3D and in one of the predecessors of P3E the BK could have moved West instead. In P3E's other predecessor pattern he could have moved away from the edge. So no B-optimal predecessors exist.

P3F←P4: Black's move is forced.

P4←P5A-P5C: deletions from P4's candidate predecessor set (see generation rules in text) occur because the positions concerned allow immediate transition to pattern P2 or pattern P0.

P5A-P5C ← □ : in all the predecessor positions of each pattern Black would have been free to stay away from, or move away from, the edge. So all the B-optimal predecessor sets are empty.

BK-Black king, WK-White king

○→ indicates an eastward row of rook stations of which the marked square is the extreme west element.

○↓ indicates a southward row of rook stations of which the marked square is the extreme north element.

↘○ indicates a sub-array of rook stations of which the marked square is the extreme north-west element.

↙○→ indicates a sub-array of rook stations of which the marked square is the extreme north-east element.

□ denotes the empty set of positions.

and so on. It turns out that the tree-construction soon terminates in parentless nodes after only ten new patterns have been added to pattern 0. This is shown in figure 5, which also contains a commentary on the various arcs of the tree. These mark pattern-to-pattern transitions. The eleven patterns do not exhaust the set of patterns required to describe all legal positions of the infinite cornerless KRK problem. They do not, for example, include cases where the BK is not on the edge, nor cases where the inter-king file distance exceeds two, nor cases where the inter-king rank distance exceeds three. There exist, therefore, legal positions not represented on the tree, and from such positions no forcing sequences to checkmate can be found.

In order to convert the annotated figure into a satisfactory demonstration, it remains to specify rules for generating w-optimal and B-optimal predecessor patterns from even-numbered and odd-numbered patterns respectively. A w-optimal predecessor of a pattern is one which is linked to that pattern by a white-optimal move; a B-optimal predecessor of a pattern is one which is linked by a black-optimal move. Strict definitions are embodied in the following generating rules.

Even-numbered patterns (Black to move)

1. For each member of the given pattern p, construct the set of legal positions from which that member can be generated by a white move.

2. Form the set-union of all the sets thus computed. Call this the candidate set.

3. For each member of the candidate set generate its legal successors. If any of these matches with some pattern already on the tree and closer to the root than p, then delete that member from the candidate set.

4. Call the residual set the set of w-optimal predecessors of p, and represent it by one or more patterns.

Odd-numbered patterns (White to move)

1. For each member of the given pattern p', construct the set of legal positions from which that member can be generated by a black move.

2. Form the set-union of all the sets thus computed. Call this the candidate set.

3. For each member of the candidate set generate its legal successors. If any of these fails to match with p', then delete that member from the candidate set.

4. Call the residual set the set of B-optimal predecessors of p', and represent it by one or more patterns.

The rules as stated require extension since they call for an operation to be performed on each member of a pattern, which (since the range of rook-moves is unbounded) may have infinitely many members. The generating algorithm must therefore be able to classify members of a pattern as the same if they are distinguished only by different rook-stations in a manner which is irrelevant to play. A sufficient classification rule is to regard as the same for purposes of pattern-description all rook-stations that lie on the same rank or file at a distance of three or more squares from the nearest other piece.

Positions, Sets and Patterns

A position is represented as a list of three co-ordinate pairs, for the
BK, the WK and the WR respectively. For the BK the x co-ordinate has
the constant value *undefined* (written u or UND) on the infinite cornerless board, while the y co-ordinate has the value 0 if the BK is on the
edge, and $1, 2, 3, \dots$ if it is $1, 2, 3, \dots$ squares from the edge. The WK and
WR have their co-ordinates reckoned *from the square of the BK*, so that
the pair (i, j) denotes a square lying i steps to the east and j steps to the
south of the BK.

A pattern selects three sub-arrays of the board, a BK-array, a WK-
array and a WR-array, each of which specifies a set of possible stations
for the relevant piece. The BK-array and WK-array are typically, but
not necessarily, unit arrays, i.e. single squares. On the infinite board the
WR-array can be of infinite extent, but the infinite set of positions is
describable by a finite set of patterns. The representation of a pattern is
similar to that of a position except that in place of a pair of co-ordinates
for each piece, specifying its station, we have a pair of intervals, specifying
the sub-array within which its station lies. Thus we have the following
representations:

position 0 $(((u,u),(0,0)), ((0,0),(2,2)), ((2,\infty),(0,0)))$
position 1 $(((u,u),(0,0)), ((0,0),(2,2)), ((2,\infty),(1,\infty)))$
position 2 $(((u,u),(0,0)), ((-1,-1),(2,2)), ((1,1),(2,\infty)))$.

To detect whether a position is a member of a given pattern we
notionally generate the Cartesian product of the latter's three sub-arrays
and check whether any of the triples so generated is identical with the
triple of co-ordinate pairs which specifies the position. As a practical
computation it is only necessary to check that each co-ordinate in the
position-specification falls within the corresponding interval of the
pattern. For proceeding in the inverse direction we require a rule that
will generate from a set of positions a minimal defining set of patterns. To
do this without ambiguity is not possible except by introducing arbitrary
criteria. For example, there are four ways of partitioning the six WK-
stations of patterns P3A–P3C into three sub-arrays of which the way
followed in figure 5 is only one. The criterion adopted was to make the
partitions as near equal in size as possible by maximizing the product of
their sizes.

Optimal Infinite Cornerless KRK

Figure 5 not only outlines a proof: for the sparse set of positions
from which mate can be forced it specifies an optimal strategy for both
players. Let us consider a way of representing the knowledge expressed
by the figure in a form convenient for a program to handle.

In addition to a base of patterns, we construct a table of *advice triples*
each of the form:

POINTER TO CONDITION PATTERN	PATTERN SPECIFYING PLAUSIBILITY CLASS	POINTER TO GOAL PATTERN(S)

To retrieve a correct move, the input position is matched against the pattern addressed by the left-hand element of each stored advice triple until a condition-match is found. Legal moves permitted by the 'plausibility class' are then applied to the position in turn, matching the result in each case against the pattern addressed by the triple's right-hand member. As soon as a goal-match is found, the corresponding move is output. The complete set of patterns and advice is set out in table 3. To run this as a strategy on the machine we require procedures for generating legal moves, for matching positions with patterns, and for input and output. POP-2 functions were de-bugged on this trivial example, and then used for developing a base of patterns and advice for the infinite board with one corner.

Table 3. Pattern-base and advice list for optimal KRK on the infinite cornerless board—see text and figure 5. Meanings of symbols are as in tables 5, 6. The last symbol in each row of the advice list gives the number of steps to mate.

P0	UND	UND	0	0	0	0	2	2	MIF	-2	0	0			
P1	UND	UND	0	0	0	0	2	2	MIF	-2	1	INF			
P2	UND	UND	0	0	-1	-1	2	2	1	1	2	INF			
P3A	UND	UND	0	0	-2	-2	1	2	1	1	2	INF			
P3B	UND	UND	0	0	-2	-1	3	3	1	1	2	INF			
P3C	UND	UND	0	0	0	0	2	3	-1	-1	2	INF			
P3D	UND	UND	0	0	-1	-1	2	2	1	1	1	INF			
P3E	UND	UND	0	0	-1	-1	2	2	2	INF	2	INF			
P3F	UND	UND	0	0	-1	-1	2	2	MIF	-1	3	INF			
P4	UND	UND	0	0	0	0	2	2	MIF	0	3	INF			
P5	UND	UND	0	0	0	0	2	3	0	0	3	INF			

0	P0	0	0	0	0	0	0	0	0	0	0	0	[]	0
1	P1	0	0	0	0	0	0	0	1	0	0	0	[P0]	1
0	P2	0	0	0	1	0	0	0	0	0	0	0	[P1]	2
1	P3A	0	0	1	0	0	1	0	0	0	0	0	[P2]	3
1	P3B	1	0	0	0	1	0	0	0	0	0	0	[P2]	3
1	P3C	0	0	0	1	0	1	0	0	0	0	0	[P2]	3
1	P3D	0	0	0	0	0	0	0	1	1	0	0	[P2]	3
1	P3E	0	0	0	0	0	0	0	0	0	0	1	[P2]	3
1	P3F	0	0	0	0	0	0	0	0	0	1	0	[P2]	3
0	P4	0	0	1	0	0	0	0	0	0	0	0	[P3F]	4
1	P5	1	0	0	0	0	0	0	0	1	1	1	[P4]	5

Optimal Infinite K R K with One Corner

On the infinite board with two edges meeting at a corner mate *can* be forced. A problem originally posed by J. Bán is as follows. Suppose that the white king and rook are in the one and only corner of an infinite chessboard, while the black king is in an arbitrarily remote square: is it possible to checkmate the black king? T. Nemes (1969), from whose account the foregoing formulation is taken, continues: 'The analysis of this problem requires considerations of a topologico-geometrical nature. To mate the black king, it is necessary to drive it to one edge of the board; consequently, the white rook and king must be on the "far" side of the black king. However, a slightly more profound analysis shows that, by moving the rook to the far side of the black king, we have confined the latter into a rectangle (one of whose diagonals is subtended by the rook and the finite corner of the board). Now the white king can start and leave this rectangle (it is, of course, not confined by its own rook!) and move on until it is on the far side of the black king in both the x and the y direction. Now both white chessmen are on the far side of the black king and the black king can be driven into the finite corner and checkmated.'

A. J. Roycroft (personal communication) comments: 'When I first came across this I was unconvinced, as it seemed to say that after White has positioned his rook he need only move his king', but rightly concluded that whatever the gaps in Nemes' reasoning, he was essentially correct. Table 4 shows a strategy for achieving the first phase—getting the white chessmen to the far side of the black king—which is complete for the initial conditions shown in the table.* Under these conditions the strategy is also optimal according to the following informal reasoning.

The strategy covers the first phase of 'one-corner infinite KRK', and is concerned with creating a situation in which the BK has no move that can further increase his distance from the corner in 'city-block' units, i.e. the sum of his co-ordinates x_{BK}, y_{BK}. This requires the WK and the WR to have got 'beyond' the BK and the WR to be safe from capture. The condition is satisfied by the situation on achievement of 'goalpattern 5' of table 4, an example of which can be seen in figure 6 where the results of running an implementation of the strategy are reproduced. We first show that it is not possible to achieve such a situation in a smaller number of moves in the case that Black follows a consistent policy of flight. We then show that departures from that policy cannot gain Black anything.

The fundamental principle is that the BK can be overtaken by the WK if and only if he can be constrained to flee along lines of latitude and longitude while his pursuer is free to move diagonally. At the expense of the three rook moves White establishes just this constraint, so that if Black makes only flight moves each one of them has to be *either* due east or due south (i.e. either x_{BK} or y_{BK} is incremented, but not both). White further ensures, so long as each black move is a flight move (i.e. one that increases $x_{BK} + y_{BK}$), that all his own king moves are diagonal to the south-east. Each such move increments *both* x_{WK} *and* y_{WK}, so that when it is followed by a black flight move a net increment of one move is gained. This represents the maximum rate at which the fleeing BK can be overtaken. Remembering that Black steals extra flight moves following each of White's three rook moves, we can reckon from the initial positions of the two kings the minimum number of net increments needed to create the pre-condition, and this is equal to the total number of moves to be made by the WK. The required expression is $m_{WK} = \text{filediff}(BK, WK) + \text{rankdiff}(BK, WK) + 3$.

Before accepting m_{WK} as White's path-length under an optimal

*The condition omitted is that in which the BK stands on, or immediately adjacent to, the board's single diagonal. It is possible, although tedious, to show that a suitable complication of the same strategy will meet this case.

Table 4. Demonstration, in the form of a complete strategy, that on the infinite board with one corner the pre-conditions can be created for the standard mating sequence (see text).

	patterns	moves for White	notes
initial:	$file(WK) = rank(WK) = 0$; $file(WR) = rank(WR) = 1$; $filediff(BK, WR) \geqslant rankdiff(BK, WR)+2$	southward rook-move achieving goal-pattern 1.	1
goal-pattern 1:	$rankdiff(WR, BK) = 1$	eastward rook-move achieving goal-pattern 2.	2
goal-pattern 2:	$filediff(WR, BK) = 3 + rankdiff(WR, WK)$	if possible then south-east king-move otherwise southward king-move; repeat until goal-pattern 3 is achieved.	3
goal-pattern 3:	$rankdiff(WK, WR) = 1$	if $filediff(WR, BK) > 2$ then westward rook-move achieving $filediff(WR, BK) = 2$ otherwise southward rook-move achieving goal-pattern 4.	4
goal-pattern 4:	$rankdiff(WR, BK) = filediff(WR, WK)$	if goal-pattern 5 then exit otherwise south-east king-move; repeat until goal-pattern 5 is achieved.	5
goal-pattern 5:	$rankdiff(WK, WR) = 0$	exit	

Notes: 1. The rook sets up an east-west line in the south.
2. The rook goes east to be out of the black king's reach during the white king's first trek.
3. The white king treks south and east to cross the rook's line.
4. The rook goes further south to be out of the black king's reach during the white king's second trek.
5. The white king treks south-east to rejoin the rook; this time the black king is completely fenced in and the white king is safely on the fence.

strategy we now ask whether the BK must necessarily flee at each step. Might he not do better at some stage to switch from increasing $x_{BK} + y_{BK}$ at each move, to going back and harassing the movements of the WK? The reasons why this does not work are as follows. The only achievable harassment consists in obliging the WK to move south rather than southeast during his first trek. This might be thought to render more lengthy White's subsequent task of bringing the WK and the WR together. But the loss is more than compensated by the westward rook move after goal-pattern 3 has been achieved. Hence the length of the southward trek (and the eventual value of y_{BK}) is not increased by the BK's manoeuvres. The eventual value of x_{BK}, on the other hand, has been diminished by twice the number of westward moves made by the BK. Thus, if the BK makes moves which are other than flight moves, he not only fails to prolong phase 1 but also stores up for himself a penalty through entering upon phase 2 in a smaller confining rectangle than he need have done.

To complete the argument we have to show that the WR cannot impose the 'latitude-or-longitude' constraint on Black's flight moves at the expense of fewer than three moves. One move is necessary to set up the constraining barrier to the south, and the second rook move necessarily follows this barrier to the east if the constraint is to be maintained. This, however, leaves the BK separated from the WR by fewer files than the WK, so that the BK cannot be impeded from advancing along the barrier and capturing the WR. Therefore at least one more rook move must be required.

The next task is to chase the black king back to the corner. This proceeds in a series of cycles. There is a cycle of six steps that forces the black king one rank to the north, illustrated in figure 7. If he decides to flee due west instead of north, there is a cycle of eight steps, shown in figure 8, that forces him *two* files to the west, i.e. one file per four steps.

Alternating these two cycles according to the black king's direction of flight, we ask how many steps are required to bring the black king from a square with co-ordinates x, y to the corner. The black king will so plan his flight as to postpone the moment of contact with either edge. The reason is that once he is on an edge White can set up conditions for driving him towards the corner at the much faster rate of one rank (or file) per 2 steps. This is shown in figures 9 and 10. So if the north cycle and west cycle can be treated independently, the black king can clearly be brought to an edge in at most $4x + 6y$ steps.

Figure 11 shows the north and west cycles graphically. There is but one single position belonging to both cycles allowing Black to transfer, if he chooses, from one cycle to the other. It follows that however he exercises this option he must yield one rank for every six steps round the north cycle and two files for every eight steps round the west cycle. The cycles can be treated independently.

Table 5 shows the advice triples corresponding to the complete optimal solution of Bán's problem, operating on the pattern base set out in table 6. As in the cornerless case, to execute this advice, the input position is tested against the condition patterns until a match is found. A move compatible with the associated plausibility class is then generated and applied, and the resulting position is tested against the triple's goal pattern. If it matches, then the move is output. If not, the next compatible move is tried. In order to accommodate the predicates of table 4, the apparatus for specifying a co-ordinate interval was extended, as described in the caption of table 6.

The advice shown only caters for positions which can arise in optimal play. Output from two specimen runs of the program was given in figure 6. Figure 12 shows the last few steps in these sequences run through with output parameters set to give an 'introspective record', and figure 13 shows the flow of control through the complete set of advice. Total POP-2 text (exclusive of patterns and advice) was 685 lines.

Path-Lengths

It should be noted that m_{WK} is a function of the *sum* of the BK's original co-ordinates. Consequently all BK starting positions which have the same city-block distance from the corner must yield identically the same position at the close of phase 1, and hence the same number of steps in the complete mating path. Thus in the next problem in the sequence illustrated in figures 6a and 6b, exactly the same instance of pattern PW8 would be generated (on move 28) whether the BK started at $(6,2)$ or at $(5,3)$. The fact that path-lengths can be expressed as a function of only one parameter, namely the BK's initial co-ordinate-sum z, simplifies the numerical treatment, which is set out in table 7.

DISCUSSION

The knowledge required to give optimal solutions to Bán's problem on the infinite one-cornered chessboard was embedded in a data-base comprising only 36 advice triples referencing 28 patterns. Further compression would be possible, but scarcely profitable without a tighter specification of what constitutes a pattern. In our case an extra facility— of defining a co-ordinate class by a POP-2 function in place of an interval bounds-pair—was introduced so as to be able to break out from the language of unconditional co-ordinate intervals when required, e.g. for cases where specification of one co-ordinate requires reference to the other. Motivation is lacking for a search for principles for forming minimal sets of patterns in a patched-together description language of this kind. Search for principles with reference to a description language of greater generality is, on the other hand, a matter of importance to which we intend to return at a later stage of the investigation.

Using the crude pattern language of figures 5 and 6 it was found easy to make local changes to the strategy, and to detect and mend lapses from optimality during interactive testing of the program. More difficult problems—even KRK on the 8×8 board—will need means of automatically generating patterns. The reasons are (a) that constructing patterns from the user's head is burdensome, and in a difficult domain prohibitive. Further, the problem of guarding against human error becomes unmanageable. (b) No proof, only plausible argument, has been given of the assertion that the strategy here exhibited is optimal. For formal proof to be tractable the patterns need to be the product of a fully defined procedure. The guarantee of optimality can then be built into the generating algorithm itself.

ACKNOWLEDGEMENTS
Part of this work was done during a visit to the Department of Information Sciences, University of California, Santa Cruz, to whom my thanks are due. I also wish to acknowledge programming assistance received during my stay from Mr Michael Lawson.

REFERENCES
Bán, J. (1963) *The Tactics of End-Games* (trs. from the Hungarian by J. Bochkor). Corvina Press. Reprinted 1972 by the Athenaeum Printing House (Kultura, PO Box 149, Budapest 62).

Bramer, M. A. (1975) Representation of knowledge for chess endgames. *Technical report.* The Open University: Faculty of Mathematics (Milton Keynes, UK).

Fine, R. (1941) *Basic Chess Endings.* New York: David McKay Company, and London: G. Bell and Sons, Ltd.

Huberman, B. J. (1968) A program to play chess end games. *Technical report no. CS 106.* Stanford University: Computer Science Department.

de Latil, P. (1956) *Thinking by Machine* (trs. from the French by Y. M. Golla). London: Sidgwick and Jackson.

Nemes, T. N. (1969) *Cybernetic Machines* (trs. from the 1962 Hungarian edition by I. Földes). London: Iliffe Books Ltd.

Samuel, A. L. (1959) Some studies in machine learning using the game of checkers. *IBM J. Res. Dev. 3,* 211–29.

Shannon, C. (1950) Programming a computer for playing chess. *Phil. Mag. 41,* 356–75.

Sussman, G. J. (1975) *A computer model of skill acquisition.* Elsevier Computer Science Library, Artificial Intelligence series no. 1. New York: American Elsevier Publishing Company.

Vigneron, H. (1914) Les automates. *La Natura,* 56–61.

Zermelo, E. (1912) Über eine Anwendung der Mengenlehre auf die Theorie des Schachspiels. *Proc. 5th int. Cong. Mathematicians,* 501–4. Cambridge. (English translation in *Firbush News 6* (1976). Edinburgh: Machine Intelligence Research Unit.)

Zuidema, C. (1974) Chess, how to program the exceptions? *Afdeling informatica* IW21/74. Amsterdam: Mathematisch Centrum.

```
        Ø  1  2  3  4

Ø   WK  .  .  .  .

1   .  WR  .  .  .

2   .  .  .  .  BK
```

WHITE TO PLAY


```
BANØ
BAN1  ——— WR sets up an east-west line in the south
BAN1
BAN2  ——— WR goes east
BAN24
BAN2  ——— WK starts trek to south-east
BAN24
BAN2
BAN24
BAN2
BAN24
BAN2
BAN3  ——— WR moves south
BAN4  ⎤
BAN5  ⎟
BAN4  ⎟
BAN5  ⎟
BAN4  ⎬ Second leg of WK's trek to south-east
BAN5  ⎟
BAN4  ⎟
BAN5  ⎟
BAN4  ⎟
BAN5  ⎦
BAN4  ——— BK backs off north, giving the following position:
```


```
       Ø  1  2  3  4  5  6  7  8  9  1Ø 11  ⎤
                                            ⎟
Ø   .  .  .  .  .  .  .  .  .  .  .  .       ⎟
                                            ⎟
1   .  .  .  .  .  .  .  .  .  .  .  .       ⎟
                                            ⎟
2   .  .  .  .  .  .  .  .  .  .  .  .       ⎟    Matches with
                                            ⎟    Pattern PW8, marki
3   .  .  .  .  .  .  .  .  .  .  .  .       ⎟    the start of part
                                            ⎬    BK is fenced in,
4   .  .  .  .  .  .  .  .  .  .  .  .       ⎟    WK is safely on
                                            ⎟    the fence.
5   .  .  .  .  .  .  .  .  .  .  .  .       ⎟
                                            ⎟
6   .  .  .  .  .  .  .  .  .  .  BK  .      ⎟
                                            ⎟
7   .  .  .  .  .  .  .  .  .  .  .  .       ⎟
                                            ⎟
8   .  .  .  .  .  .  .  .  .  .  .  .       ⎟
                                            ⎟
9   .  .  .  .  .  .  .  .  .  WK  .  WR     ⎦
```

WHITE TO PLAY

```
PWB  ⎫              PN3  ⎫
PN4  ⎪              PW4  ⎪
PV5  ⎪              PN5  ⎪
PN6  ⎪              PW3  ⎪
PN1  ⎪              PNW2 ⎪
PNW2 ⎪              PN1  ⎪
─────              PN6  ⎪
PN3  ⎪              PNW2 ⎪
PN4  ⎪              ─────
PN5  ⎪              PW3  ⎪
PN6  ⎪              PW4  ⎪
PV1  ⎪              PW5  ⎪
PNW2 ⎪              PW3  ⎪
─────              PNW2 ⎪
PN3  ⎪              PN1  ⎪
PN4  ⎪              PN6  ⎪
PN5  ⎬ 5 'north cycles'   PNW2 ⎪
PN6  ⎪              ───── ⎬ 4 'west cycles'
PN1  ⎪              PW3  ⎪
PNW2 ⎪              PW4  ⎪
─────              PW5  ⎪
PN3  ⎪              PW3  ⎪
PN4  ⎪              PNW2 ⎪
PN5  ⎪              PN1  ⎪
PN6  ⎪              PN6  ⎪
PN1  ⎪              PNW2 ⎪
PNW2 ⎪              ─────
─────              PN3  ⎪
PN3  ⎪              PW4  ⎪
PN4  ⎪              PN5  ⎪
PN5  ⎪              PW3  ⎪
PN6  ⎪              PNW2 ⎪
PN1  ⎪              PN1  ⎪
PNW2 ⎭              PN6  ⎪
─────              PNW2 ⎭
PW3  ⎫              PNC0 ⎫
PW4  ⎪              PNC1 ⎪
PW5  ⎪              PWC4 ⎪
PW3  ⎪              PWC6 ⎬ Terminal
PNW2 ⎪              PWC7 ⎪  manoeuvre
PN1  ⎬ Transition   PNC10 ⎪
PNC6 ⎪  manoeuvre  PNC11 ⎪
PN4  ⎪              PWC8 ⎭
PV5  ⎪
PN6  ⎪        END OF PLAY: TOTAL OF 105 STEPS
PN1  ⎪
PNW2 ⎭
```

```
      0  1  2

 0  BK  .  .

 1  .  .  WK

 2  WR  .  .
```

TERMINAL POSITION

Figure 6a. Output of the program when applied to an instance of Bán's problem (top left). Print-out shows successive pattern matches, with annotations corresponding to the categories of tables 4 and 7.

```
      0   1   2   3   4   5

0  WK  .   .   .   .   .

1   .  WR  .   .   .   .

2   .   .   .   .   .  BK
```

WHITE TO PLAY

```
BAN0
BAN1
BAN1
BAN2
BAN2A
BAN2
BAN2A
BAN2
BAN2A
BAN2
BAN2A
BAN2
BAN3
BAN4
BAN5
BAN4
BAN5
BAN4
BAN5
BAN4
BAN5
BAN4
BAN5
BAN4
BAN5
BAN4
```

```
      0   1   2   3   4   5   6   7   8   9  10  11  12

0   .   .   .   .   .   .   .   .   .   .   .   .   .

1   .   .   .   .   .   .   .   .   .   .   .   .   .

2   .   .   .   .   .   .   .   .   .   .   .   .   .

3   .   .   .   .   .   .   .   .   .   .   .   .   .

4   .   .   .   .   .   .   .   .   .   .   .   .   .

5   .   .   .   .   .   .   .   .   .   .   .   .   .

6   .   .   .   .   .   .   .   .   .   .   .   .   .

7   .   .   .   .   .   .   .   .   .   .   .  BK   .

8   .   .   .   .   .   .   .   .   .   .   .   .   .

9   .   .   .   .   .   .   .   .   .   .   .   .   .

10  .   .   .   .   .   .   .   .   .  WK   .  WR
```

WHITE TO PLAY

PW8	PW3	PW3
PN4	PW4	PW4
PN5	PW5	PW5
PN6	PW3	PW3
PN1	PNW2	PNW2
PNW2	PN1	PN1
PN3	PNC6	PN6
PN4	PN4	PNW2
PN5	PN5	PW3
PN6	PN6	PW4
PN1	PN1	PW6
PNW2	PNW2	PNC3
PN3	PW3	PNW2
PN4	PW4	PN1
PN5	PW5	PNC11
PN6	PW3	PWC8
PN1	PNW2	PNC12
PNW2	PN1	PNC11
PN3	PN6	PNC10
PN4	PNW2	PNC10
PN5	PW3	PNC11
PN6	PW4	PWC8
PN1	PW5	
PNW2	PW3	
PN3	PNW2	END OF PLAY:
PN4	PN1	TOTAL OF 119 STEPS
PN5	PN6	
PN6	PNW2	
PN1	PW3	
PNW2	PW4	
PN3	PW5	
PN4	PW3	
PN5	PNW2	
PN6	PN1	
PN1	PN6	
PNW2	PNW2	

```
          0   1   2

  0   BK   .   .

  1   .    .   WK

  2   WR   .   .

TERMINAL POSITION
```

Figure 6b. Output obtained from a starting position differing in parity to that of figure 6a. This difference is the cause of the divergence of the two terminal sequences, shown in detail in figures 12a and 12b.

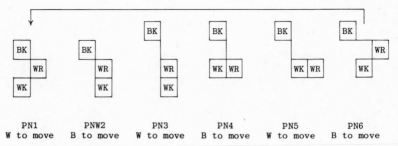

Figure 7. The 'north cycle' of six steps that forces Black to yield one
rank per cycle.

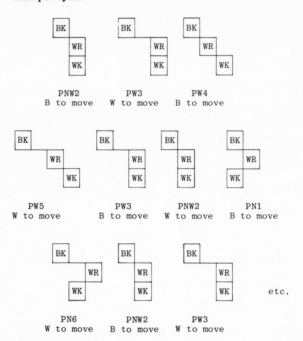

Figure 8. The 'west cycle' of eight steps which forces the black king to
yield two files per cycle.

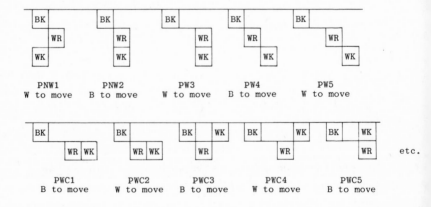

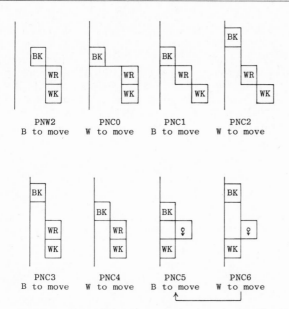

Figure 10. When the black king emerges from a west cycle on to the west edge, as occurs above at PNC0, the WR sets up a north-south corridor one square wide along which the WK chases the BK at the rate of one rank per two steps.

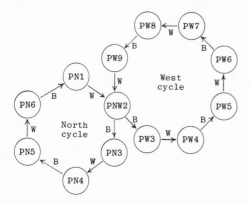

Figure 11. Graphic representation of the two forcing cycles. The arcs are labelled according to the move, and the nodes according to the conventions of figures 7 and 8.

Figure 9. If the black king were to hit the north edge in the course of a 'north cycle' (optimal KRK avoids this) the WR would set up an east-west corridor one square wide, along which the BK can be chased at the rate of one file per two steps.

Table 5. Advice list for solution of Bán's problem. The first digit of each piece of advice, 1 or 0, denotes whether it is w or b to play. Then follows the identifier of the left-hand, or 'condition', pattern. The sequence of twelve binary digits that follows defines the 'plausibility class' according to the code: North South East West NE SE NW SW North South East West. The first eight symbols refer to king moves (w or b as the case may be). The last four symbols refer to rook-moves in the case that w is to play; otherwise they are set to zero. The 'target list' follows, enclosed in square brackets. The last component, 'steps to mate', is not shown.

play	condition	N	S	E	W	NE	SE	NW	SW	N	S	E	W	target list	
1	BAN3	0	0	0	0	0	0	0	0	0	1	0	0	[BAN1]	⎫
0	BAN1	0	0	1	0	0	0	0	0	0	0	0	0	[BAN1]	
1	BAN1	0	0	0	0	0	0	0	0	0	1	0		[BAN2]	
0	BAN2	0	0	1	0	0	0	0	0	0	0	0	0	[BAN2A BAN3]	part A:
1	BAN2A	0	0	0	0	0	1	0	0	0	0	0	0	[BAN2]	outward bound
1	BAN3	0	0	0	0	0	0	0	0	0	1	0	0	[BAN4]	
0	BAN4	1	1	0	0	0	0	0	0	0	0	0	0	[BAN5 PW8]	
1	BAN5	0	0	0	0	1	1	0	0	0	0	0	0	[BAN4]	⎭
1	PW8	0	0	0	0	1	0	0	0	0	0	0	0	[PN4]	transitional
0	PN4	0	0	0	1	0	0	0	0	0	0	0	0	[PN5]	⎫
1	PN5	0	0	0	0	0	0	0	0	1	0	0	0	[PN6]	
0	PN6	0	0	1	0	0	0	0	0	0	0	0	0	[PN1]	part B:
1	PN1	0	0	1	0	0	0	0	0	0	0	0	0	[PNW2]	north cycle
0	PNW2	1	0	0	1	0	0	0	0	0	0	0	0	[PN3 PW3 PNC0]	
1	PN3	0	0	0	0	0	0	1	0	0	0	0	0	[PN4]	⎭
1	PW3	0	0	0	0	0	0	0	0	0	1	0	0	[PW4]	⎫
0	PW4	1	0	0	1	0	0	0	0	0	0	0	0	[PW6 PW5]	
1	PW5	1	0	0	0	0	0	0	0	0	0	0	0	[PW3 PNC0]	
0	PW3	0	1	0	0	0	0	0	0	0	0	0	0	[PNW2]	part C:
1	PNW2	0	0	0	1	0	0	0	0	0	0	0	0	[PN1]	west cycle
0	PN1	1	0	0	1	0	0	0	0	0	0	0	0	[PN6 PNC6 PNC11]	
1	PN6	0	0	0	0	0	0	0	0	0	0	0	1	[PNW2]	⎭
1	PNC6	1	0	0	0	0	0	0	0	0	0	0	0	[PN4]	transitional
1	PW6	0	0	0	1	0	0	0	0	0	0	0	0	[PNC0]	⎫
0	PNC0	0	0	1	0	0	0	0	0	0	0	0	0	[PNW2]	
1	PNC11	0	0	0	0	1	0	0	0	1	0	0	0	[PWC8]	
0	PWC8	1	0	0	0	0	0	0	0	0	0	0	0	[PNC12]	
1	PNC12	1	0	0	0	0	0	0	0	0	0	0	0	[PNC11]	
0	PNC11	0	0	1	0	0	0	0	0	0	0	0	0	[PNC10]	terminal
1	PNC10	0	0	0	0	0	0	0	0	0	1	0		[PNC10]	manoeuvres
0	PNC10	1	0	0	0	0	0	0	0	0	0	0	0	[PNC11]	
1	PNC0	0	0	0	0	0	0	0	0	0	0	0	1	[PNC1]	
0	PNC1	1	0	0	0	0	0	0	0	0	0	0	0	[PWC4 PNC2]	
1	PWC4	1	0	0	0	0	0	0	0	0	0	0	0	[PWC6]	
0	PWC6	0	1	0	0	0	0	0	0	0	0	0	0	[PWC7]	
1	PWC7	1	0	0	0	0	0	0	0	0	0	0	0	[PNC10]	⎭

Table 6. Pattern-base for Bán's problem. The pattern number is in each case followed by twelve symbols, four for each of the pieces BK, WK and WR. For each piece the first two symbols set the range within which the piece's first co-ordinate (specifying the east-west bearing) must fall, and the second sets the range for the second co-ordinate. Ranges are ordinarily defined by pairs of integers: UND, MIF and INF denote 'undefined', 'minus infinity' and 'infinity' respectively. Exceptionally the symbol 'P' is used as the first member of a pair to indicate that the second member is a call to a POP-2 truth-function (see text).

BAN0	UND	UND	P	F3	MIF	-3	MIF	-1	MIF	-2	MIF	-1
BAN1	UND	UND	UND	UND	MIF	-3	MIF	-1	MIF	-2	1	1
BAN2	UND	UND	UND	UND	MIF	-3	MIF	2	P	F1	1	1
BAN2A	UND	UND	UND	UND	MIF	-3	MIF	2	2	INF	1	1
BAN3	UND	UND	UND	UND	MIF	-3	2	2	1	1	1	1
BAN4	UND	UND	UND	UND	MIF	-1	1	2	1	1	P	F2
BAN5	UND	UND	UND	UND	MIF	-1	1	2	1	1	2	INF
PW8	1	INF	1	INF	-1	-1	3	3	1	1	3	3
PN4	1	INF	1	INF	0	0	2	2	1	1	2	INF
PN5	1	INF	1	INF	1	1	2	2	2	2	2	INF
PN6	1	INF	1	INF	1	1	2	2	2	2	1	1
PN1	1	INF	1	INF	0	0	2	2	1	1	1	1
PNW2	0	INF	1	INF	1	1	2	2	1	1	1	1
PN3	1	INF	2	INF	1	1	3	3	1	1	2	2
PW3	1	INF	1	INF	2	2	2	2	1	1	2	2
PW4	1	INF	1	INF	2	2	2	2	1	1	1	1
PW5	1	INF	1	INF	2	2	3	3	1	1	2	2
PNC6	1	INF	1	INF	0	0	3	3	1	1	2	INF
PW6	0	0	1	INF	3	3	2	2	2	2	1	1
PNC0	0	0	1	2	2	2	2	2	2	2	1	1
PNC11	0	0	0	INF	1	1	2	2	2	2	1	INF
PWC8	0	0	0	INF	1	1	2	2	2	2	0	0
PNC12	0	0	0	INF	1	1	3	3	2	2	1	INF
PNC10	0	0	1	3	2	2	0	0	1	INF	1	1
PNC1	0	0	1	INF	2	2	2	2	1	1	1	1
PWC4	0	0	0	2	2	2	3	3	1	1	2	2
PWC6	0	0	0	2	2	2	2	2	1	1	2	2
PWC7	0	0	1	INF	2	2	1	1	1	1	1	1

Table 7. Breakdown of the optimal path-lengths of solutions to Bán's problem. The initial co-ordinates are assumed to be WK: $(0, 0)$; WR: $(1, 1)$; BK: (x, y) such that $x - y \geqslant 2$; $z = x + y$. $p(z)$ is the 'parity' of z, i.e. 1 if z is odd and 0 if z is even.

		no. of steps in optimal path
part A: outward bound	WR moves:	3
	WK moves:	$z + 3$
	BK moves:	$z + 6$
	total, part A	$2z + 12$
part B: north cycles		$6z - 6$
part C: transition manoeuvre		12
part D: west cycles		$4z + 8 - 4p(z)$
part E: terminal manoeuvre		$7 + 6p(z)$
	total overall	$12z + 33 + 2p(z)$

```
     0  1  2
0    .  .  .
1  BK  .  .
2    .  . WR
3    .  . WK
```

WHITE TO PLAY

POSITION MATCHES PNC0

7 MOVES TO MATE.   TARGLIST:[PNC1]
W KING MOVES: NO PLAUSIBLE MOVES.
ROOK MOVES: TRYING WEST
MATCH FOUND WITH TARGET PNC1

```
     0  1  2
0    .  .  .
1  BK  .  .
2    . WR  .
3    .  . WK
```

BLACK TO PLAY

POSITION MATCHES PNC1

6 MOVES TO MATE.   TARGLIST:[PWC4 PNC2]
B KING MOVES: TRYING NORTH
MATCH FOUND WITH TARGET PWC4

```
     0  1  2
0  BK  .  .
1    .  .  .
2    . WR  .
3    .  . WK
```

WHITE TO PLAY

POSITION MATCHES PWC4

5 MOVES TO MATE.   TARGLIST:[PWC6]
W KING MOVES: TRYING NORTH
MATCH FOUND WITH TARGET PWC6

```
     0  1  2
0  BK  .  .
1    .  .  .
2    . WR WK
```

BLACK TO PLAY

POSITION MATCHES PWC6

4 MOVES TO MATE.   TARGLIST:[PWC7]
B KING MOVES: TRYING SOUTH
MATCH FOUND WITH TARGET PWC7

```
     0  1  2
0    .  .  .
1  BK  .  .
2    . WR WK
```

WHITE TO PLAY

POSITION MATCHES PWC7

3 MOVES TO MATE.   TARGLIST:[PNC10]
W KING MOVES: TRYING NORTH
MATCH FOUND WITH TARGET PNC10

```
     0  1  2
0    .  .  .
1  BK  . WK
2    . WR  .
```

BLACK TO PLAY

POSITION MATCHES PNC10

2 MOVES TO MATE.   TARGLIST:[PNC11 PW■
B KING MOVES: TRYING NORTH
MATCH FOUND WITH TARGET PNC11

```
     0  1  2
0  BK  .  .
1    .  . WK
2    . WR  .
```

WHITE TO PLAY

POSITION MATCHES PNC11

1 MOVES TO MATE.   TARGLIST:[PWC8]
W KING MOVES: TRYING SW
NO MATCH WITH TARG.
ROOK MOVES: TRYING WEST
MATCH FOUND WITH TARGET PWC8

```
     0  1  2
0  BK  .  .
1    .  . WK
2  WR  .  .
```

BLACK TO PLAY

POSITION MATCHES PWC8

0 MOVES TO MATE.   TARGLIST:[PNC12]
B KING MOVES: TRYING WEST
NO MATCH WITH TARG.

END OF PLAY: TOTAL OF 105 STEPS

Figure 12a. Terminal sequence of figure 6a run with program parameters set to full output.

```
0  1  2  3
.  BK  .  .

.  .  . WK

.  . WR  .
```

ITE TO PLAY

OSITION MATCHES PNC11

MOVES TO MATE. TARGLIST:[PWC8]
KING MOVES: TRYING SW
O MATCH WITH TARG.
OOK MOVES: TRYING WEST
ATCH FOUND WITH TARGET PWC8

```
0  1  2  3
.  BK  .  .

.  .  . WK

. WR  .  .
```

LACK TO PLAY

OSITION MATCHES PWC8

MOVES TO MATE. TARGLIST:[PNC12]
KING MOVES: TRYING WEST
ATCH FOUND WITH TARGET PNC12

```
0  1  2  3
BK  .  .  .

.  .  . WK

. WR  .  .
```

ITE TO PLAY

OSITION MATCHES PNC12

MOVES TO MATE. TARGLIST:[PNC11]
KING MOVES: TRYING WEST
ATCH FOUND WITH TARGET PNC11

```
0  1  2
BK  .  .

.  . WK

. WR  .
```

LACK TO PLAY

OSITION MATCHES PNC11

MOVES TO MATE. TARGLIST:[PNC10]
KING MOVES: TRYING SOUTH
ATCH FOUND WITH TARGET PNC10

```
     0  1  2
0    .  .  .

1   BK  . WK

2    . WR  .
```

WHITE TO PLAY

POSITION MATCHES PNC10

3 MOVES TO MATE. TARGLIST:[PNC10]
W KING MOVES: NO PLAUSIBLE MOVES.
ROOK MOVES: TRYING EAST
MATCH FOUND WITH TARGET PNC10

```
     0  1  2
0    .  .  .

1   BK  . WK

2    .  . WR
```

BLACK TO PLAY

POSITION MATCHES PNC10

2 MOVES TO MATE. TARGLIST:[PNC11 PWC2]
B KING MOVES: TRYING NORTH
MATCH FOUND WITH TARGET PNC11

```
     0  1  2
0   BK  .  .

1    .  . WK

2    .  . WR
```

WHITE TO PLAY

POSITION MATCHES PNC11

1 MOVES TO MATE. TARGLIST:[PWC8]
W KING MOVES: TRYING SW
NO MATCH WITH TARG.
ROOK MOVES: TRYING WEST
MATCH FOUND WITH TARGET PWC8

```
     0  1  2
0   BK  .  .

1    .  . WK

2   WR  .  .
```

BLACK TO PLAY

POSITION MATCHES PWC8

0 MOVES TO MATE. TARGLIST:[PNC12]
B KING MOVES: TRYING WEST
NO MATCH WITH TARG.

END OF PLAY: TOTAL OF 119 STEPS

Figure 12b. Terminal sequence of figure 6b. Essentially the same sequence as that of figure 6a is entered, but displaced one square to the east. Thus, when the pattern PNC11 is reached (top left), and then PWC8, the BK has flight squares, and six additional steps are required to reach checkmate.

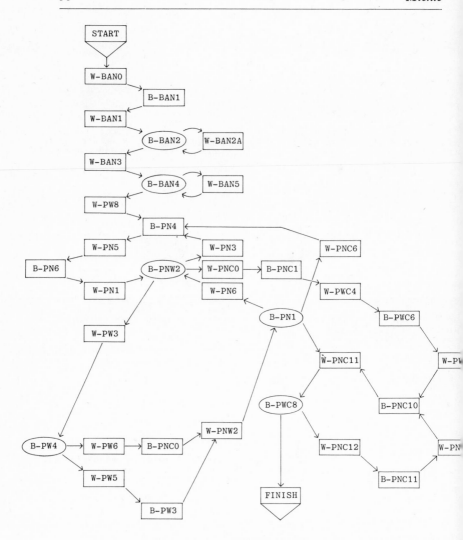

Figure 13. Complete strategy for Bán's problem. It divides into parts as follows:

Part A. *Outward bound*: the sequence from w–BAN0 to exit to w–PW8 (goalpatterns 1 and 5 respectively of table 4). The two cycles represent the BK's eastward and southward journeys respectively.

Part B. *North cycle*: this is B–PN4→w–PN5→B–PN6→w–PN1→B–PNW2 →w–PN3, with B–PNW2 acting as the transfer point for entry to the west cycle.

West cycle: on the first time round this cycle, which starts B–PNW2→w–PW3→B–PW4→w–PW5, Black gains time by playing to w–PNC6 rather than w–PN6. This is referred to in the text as the 'transition manoeuvre'.

Terminal manoeuvre: the end-play follows different routes according to the parity of the starting position. For $z = 5, 7, 9, 11, \ldots$ we have w–PW6→B–PNC0→w–PNW2→B–PN1→w–PNC11→B–PWC8→ w–PNC12 etc. For $z = 6, 8, 10, 12, \ldots$ we have w–PNC0→B–PNC1→ w–PWC4→B–PWC6 etc.

Appendix. Computer Simulation of
Torres y Quevedo's KRK Machine

Specimen play from the Torres strategy (figure 3 of the main text) was obtained by hand-simulation from table 1. As a check, the six decision rules were then re-expressed as an advice-list, shown in table 8, suitable for use with the program. The same sequence of moves were generated by program as had been found by hand. Only White's moves were computed, since Torres' rules only apply to White, and this is reflected in the advice-list. Black's replies were typed into the program using a 'request for suggestions' option, which the program invokes when it cannot find any matching advice for an input position.

Simulating the Torres machine was an interesting supplementary exercise in expressing a strategy as a data file for the advice-taking program. Implementing the strategy itself was quick and easy enough, all the non-Torres-specific work having already been done in writing the main program. On the other hand the limitation of descriptive form to conjunctions of predicates defined on individual co-ordinates was felt to be distinctly cramping. More complex domains than KRK will require less restrictive formats.

Table 8. Torres' strategy as patterns-and-advice files.

```
TOR0  0  7  0  5  UND  UND  2  7  P  Q3  UND  UND
TOR1  P  Q5  0  5  UND  UND  2  7  P  Q6  UND  UND
TOR2  0  7  0  4  UND  UND  3  7  UND  UND  2  6
TOR3  0  7  0  5  UND  UND  3  7  UND  UND  1  1
TOR4  0  7  0  5  0  0  2  2  UND  UND  1  1
TOR5  0  7  0  5  0  0  2  2  UND  UND  0  0
TOR7  0  7  0  5  P  Q1  2  7  P  Q4  1  1
TOR8  0  7  0  5  P  Q2  2  7  UND  UND  1  1

Q1:  IS  BK  FILE  DISTANCE  ODD?

Q2:  IS  BK  FILE  DISTANCE  NON-ZERO  AND  EVEN?

Q3:  IS  PIECE  ON  SIDE  OF  THE  BOARD?

Q4:  DOES  BK  FILE  DISTANCE  EXCEED  1?

Q5  IS  PIECE  IN  ONE  OF  THE  TWO  "ZONES"?

Q6:  IS  PIECE  IN  SAME  ZONE  AS  BK?


1  TOR8  0  0  1  0  0  0  0  0  0  0  0  0  [TOR7]
1  TOR7  0  0  0  0  0  0  0  0  0  0  1  1  [TOR7]
1  TOR4  0  0  0  0  0  0  0  0  1  0  0  0  [TOR5]
1  TOR3  1  0  0  0  0  0  0  0  0  0  0  0  [TOR3 TOR4 TOR7 TOR8]
1  TOR2  0  0  0  0  0  0  0  0  1  0  0  0  [TOR2 TOR3]
1  TOR1  0  0  0  0  0  0  0  0  0  0  1  1  [TOR0]
```

Positional Play in Chess by Computer

R.H.Atkin

The game of chess can be viewed as an example of an hierarchical structure (Atkin 1975). By this we mean the following scheme, in which each level is to be well-defined in terms of the one beneath it:

level	nature of play	relation
$N+2$	super-positional play	$\Sigma\ W'' \times S''$
$N+1$	positional play	$\Lambda\ W' \times S'$
N	tactical play	$\Gamma\ W \times S$

At the $(N+2)$-level we expect to be able to assess (and to rank) the $(N+1)$-level structure. At the $(N+1)$-level we expect to be able to assess (and to rank) the N-level structure. This will mean, if we are successful, that if moves at the tactical level (N) are evaluated (by some evaluation function) then good positional (and super-positional) play tells us *how to produce an evaluation function*. The role of the $(N+2)$-level is to tell us how to change our assessment of the $(N+1)$-positional features and therefore it tells us *when* to change the evaluation function.

In this table the sets W, S denote the (white) chessmen and the 64 squares, respectively. The relation Γ embodies the rules of the game and has been defined in Atkin (1972) and further discussed in Atkin and Witten (1973). This relation Γ (more precisely Γ_W, for White) defines two conjugate simplicial complexes:

$K_W(S)$, described as 'White's view of the board'; and

$K_S(W)$, described as 'board's view of White'.

Naturally there are two further structures involved in the game, corresponding to the relation Γ_B, and these are

$K_B(S)$, Black's view of the board; and

$K_S(B)$, board's view of Black.

Let $W = \{W_i;\ i = 1,2,\ldots 16\}$ be the set of white men, and $S = \{S_j;\ j = 1,2,\ldots 64\}$ be the set of squares on the board. Then we define the relation $\Gamma_W \subset W \times S$ in the following way:

$$(W_i, S_j) \in \Gamma_W \text{ if and only if } W_i \text{ 'attacks' } S_j.$$

By 'attacks' we mean that one of the following holds true: (a) if it is White's move, and W_i is a piece (not the king or a pawn), then 'W_i moves to square S_j' is a legal move; (b) if W_i is a pawn then S_j is a 'capturing square' for W_i; (c) if there is a white man, $W_k(k \neq i)$, on S_j then W_i is protecting W_k, in the ordinary sense of chess-players' parlance; (d) if W_i is the white king (wK) then S_j is an immediate neighbour to the square occupied by W_i, horizontally, vertically, or diagonally; (e) if S_j contains a black man, $B_k(\neq \text{BK})$, and if it is White's move, then 'W_i

captures B_k' is a legal move; (f) the BK is on S_j and is in check to W_i.

In the paper already quoted, this relation Γ (and the associated structures $K_W(S)$ and $K_S(W)$) was used to define an *evaluation function* for each mode (I,J) of the game $((I,J)$ means that White has made I moves and Black has made J moves). This was achieved in the following way.

For a particular mode (I,J) define maps associated with the structures, viz.:

(i) on $K_W(S)$, stval: $S \rightarrow Z$ (Z being the integers)
this to give the 'strength-value' of each square $S_i \in S$

(ii) on $K_W(S)$, pval: $W \rightarrow Z$
this to give the 'piece-value' of each piece $W_i \in W$

(iii) on $K_S(W)$, cval: $W \rightarrow Z$
this to give the 'control-value' of each piece $W_i \in W$

(iv) on $K_S(W)$, sval: $S \rightarrow Z$
this to give the 'square-value' of each square $S_i \in S$.

Each such mapping is a *graded pattern* on the appropriate structure, viz.:

stval is a 0-graded pattern, π^0, on the vertices of $K_W(S)$

pval is a t-graded pattern, π^t, where t is the dimension of W in $K_W(S)$

cval is a 0-graded pattern, π^0, on the vertices of $K_S(W)$

sval is a t-graded pattern, π^t, where t is the dimension of S in $K_S(W)$.

In addition we allow for the 'inverse' relation between (e.g.) pval and cval by requiring

pval(W) . cval(W) = h (a fixed constant), and

sval(S) . stval(S) = k (a fixed constant).

Since, in $K_W(S)$, each W is a t-simplex (for some value of t) and is written

$$W = \langle S_{\alpha_0} S_{\alpha_1} \ldots S_{\alpha_t} \rangle$$

we take

$$\text{pval}(W) = \sum_{S_i \in W} \text{stval}(S_i)$$

and similarly,

$$\text{sval}(S) = \sum_{W_i \in S} \text{cval}(W_i)$$

where

$$S = \langle \ldots W_i \ldots \rangle.$$

The basis for the eventual evaluation function on (I,J) then rests upon the mutual relation between these four mappings and this is illustrated in the following diagram:

Various structural properties of $K_W(S)$, and ultimately of $K_B(S)$ also, are then evaluated by these four mappings. Initially the above circuit is entered in some simple-minded way, for example, by taking pval(W_i) = {1, 3, 3, 5, 9} according as W_i is a {P, B, N, R, Q}. But this is not necessary and, indeed, in a good positional player we would expect the positional assessment of the mode (I, J) to provide us with a criterion for breaking into the above diagram.

The structural features of $K_W(S)$ which have been used so far include the following: (i) Changes in the component values $\mathbf{Q}_r$ of the *structure vector* $\mathbf{Q}$ of $K_W(S)$, r taking values from 0 to 6; (ii) Sum of cval(W_i) − cval(B_j) for all white and black pieces; (iii) Sum of sval(S_i) for specific squares S_i, e.g. squares in the centre, squares occupied by opponent's pieces, opponent's king flight squares, squares on 5th, 6th, 7th ranks, squares on key diagonals. But, here again, we would expect that a good positional player (computer or human) would provide a variety of rankings of such structural features—changing with the mode (I, J).

The general approach requires us to provide what we might call a Positional Evaluation Package (PEP), based on the square of four mappings. PEP will therefore contain (figure 1):

(a) a set of weighting parameters $F = \{f_i; i = 0, 1, ..., 6\}$ together with a function

$$f = \sum_{i=0}^{6} f_i \cdot (\Delta\mathbf{Q}_i)$$

where $\Delta\mathbf{Q}_i$ denotes the increase in the ith component of the *structure vector* $\mathbf{Q}$ of $K_W(S)$;

(b) a set of weighting parameters $G = \{g_i; i = 1, ..., 16\}$ together with a function

$$g = \sum_{i=1}^{16} g_i \cdot \text{cval}(W_i)$$

(c) a set of weighting parameters $H = \{h_i; i \in I_1 \cup I_2 \cup ... \cup I_k\}$ together with functions $\{h^j\}$ where

$$h^j = \sum_{i \in I_j} h_i \cdot \text{sval}(S_i)$$

and where the index sets I_j are to be defined in terms of elements chosen from S'.

Since all the above refer only to White's structures $K_W(S)$ and $K_S(W)$ we can also incorporate Black's positional features by, for

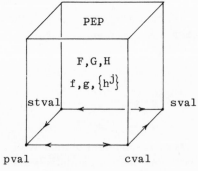

Figure 1. The positional evaluation package (PEP)

example, the corresponding functions $-f$, $-g$, $-h^j$. Then finally we assess the *positional value* (PV) by the algebraic sum, over White and over Black, of these mappings f, g, h^j (for all appropriate values of j).

At the $(N+1)$-level the set W' is a cover of the set W, that is to say, $W' = \{w_i\}$ and $\bigcup_i w_i = W$. Similarly S' is a cover of S, so that $S' = \{s_j\}$ and $\bigcup_j s_j = S$. The elements of W' and S' are those commonly used by chess players, and are listed below. Some are illustrated in figure 2.

name of element of W'		*subset of W*
w_1	king	(WK)
w_2	queen	(WQ)
w_3	rooks	(WQR, WKR, WQ)
w_4	black-square bishops	(WQB, WQ)
w_5	white-square bishops	(WKB, WQ)
w_6	knights	(WQN, WKN)
w_7	Q-side pawns	(pawns on Q-side)
w_8	K-side pawns	(pawns on K-side)
w_9	centre pawns	(pawns on d4, d5, e4, e5)
w_{10}	central pawns	(pawns in QB-, Q-, K-, KB-files)

name of element of S'		*subset of S*
s_1	centre	{d4, d5, e4, e5}
s_2	rank 1	{a1, b1, ..., h1}
s_3	rank 2	{a2, b2, ..., h2}
s_4	rank 3	{a3, b3, ..., h3}
s_5	rank 4	{a4, b4, ..., h4}
s_6	rank 5	{a5, b5, ..., h5}
s_7	rank 6	{a6, b6, ..., h6}
s_8	rank 7	{a7, b7, ..., h7}
s_9	rank 8	{a8, b8, ..., h8}
s_{10}	QR-file	{a1, a2, ..., a8}
s_{11}	QN-file	{b1, b2, ..., b8}
s_{12}	QB-file	{c1, c2, ..., c8}
s_{13}	Q-file	{d1, d2, ..., d8}
s_{14}	K-file	{e1, e2, ..., e8}
s_{15}	KB-file	{f1, f2, ..., f8}
s_{16}	KN-file	{g1, g2, ..., g8}
s_{17}	KR-file	{h1, h2, ..., h8}
s_{18}	diagonal w1	{b1, a2}
s_{19}	diagonal B1	{c1, b2, a3}
s_{20}	diagonal w2	{d1, c2, b3, a4}
s_{21}	diagonal B2	{e1, d2, c3, b4, a5}
s_{22}	diagonal w3	{f1, e2, d3, c4, b5, a6}
s_{23}	diagonal B3	{g1, f2, e3, d4, c5, b6, a7}
s_{24}	diagonal w4	{h1, g2, f3, e4, d5, c6, b7, a8}
s_{25}	diagonal B4	{h2, g3, f4, e5, d6, c7, b8}

name of element of S'		*subset of S*
s_{26}	diagonal w5	{ h3, g4, f5, e6, d7, c8 }
s_{27}	diagonal B5	{ h4, g5, f6, e7, d8 }
s_{28}	diagonal w6	{ h5, g6, f7, e3 }
s_{29}	diagonal B6	{ h6, g7, f8 }
s_{30}	diagonal w7	{ h7, g8 }
s_{31}	diagonal B7	{ g1, h2 }
s_{32}	diagonal w8	{ f1, g2, h3 }
s_{33}	diagonal B8	{ e1, f2, g3, h4 }
s_{34}	diagonal w9	{ d1, e2, f3, g4, h5 }
s_{35}	diagonal B9	{ c1, d2, e3, f4, g5, h6 }
s_{36}	diagonal w10	{ b1, c2, d3, e4, f5, g6, h7 }
s_{37}	diagonal B10	{ a1, b2, c3, d4, e5, f6, g7, h8 }
s_{38}	diagonal w11	{ a2, b3, c4, d5, e6, f7, g8 }
s_{39}	diagonal B11	{ a3, b4, c5, d6, e7, f8 }
s_{40}	diagonal w12	{ a4, b5, c6, d7, e8 }
s_{41}	diagonal B12	{ a5, b6, c7, d8 }
s_{42}	diagonal w13	{ a6, b7, c8 }
s_{43}	diagonal B13	{ a7, b8 }
s_{44}	enemy pawn positions	$(S_i : pos(\text{BP}) = S_i)$
s_{45}	enemy knight positions	$(S_i : pos(\text{BN}) = S_i)$
s_{46}	enemy bishop positions	$(S_i : pos(\text{BB}) = S_i)$
s_{47}	enemy rook positions	$(S_i : pos(\text{BR}) = S_i)$
s_{48}	enemy queen positions	$(S_i : pos(\text{BQ}) = S_i)$
s_{49}	enemy king positions	$(S_i : pos(\text{BK}) = S_i)$
s_{50}	enemy K-simplex in	$(S_i : (\text{BK}, S_i) \in \Gamma')$
s_{51}	weak Black P-control	$(S_i : (S_i, \text{BP}) \notin \Gamma_B \ \& \ S_i \in \{s_5, s_6, s_7\})$

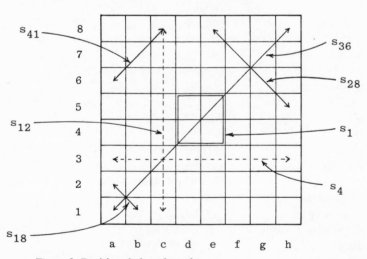

Figure 2. Positional chess board

The relation Λ, at the $(N+1)$-level, is a weighted relation and defined in the following way:

(i) Λ is represented by a matrix with entries Λ_{ij}.

(ii) If $i \in \{2,3,4,5\}$ and $(w_i, s_j) \in \Lambda$ then there exist elements (W_α, S_β) such that $W_\alpha \in w_i$, $S_\beta \in s_j$ and $(W_\alpha, S_\beta) \in \Gamma'$ for all $S_\beta \in s_j$ other than the square occupied by W_α.

(iii) Γ', for any piece W_α, is Γ when only W_α is on the board.

(iv) If $i \in \{1,6,7,8,9,10\}$ and $(w_i, s_j) \in \Lambda$ then there exists (W_α, S_β) such that $W_\alpha \in w_i$ and $S_\beta \in s_j$.

(v) If I is the index set $\{(\alpha, \beta)\}$ of all pairs found under (ii) or (iv) then $\Lambda_{ij} =$ number of elements in I.

Incidentally we notice, under (ii), that Γ' can be chosen so that W_α 'sees through' either White or Black (or both).

The definition of Λ must be derivable from the definition of Γ, as it is, and it must be such that it can express standard positional ideas, such as the following:

1. A rook on the 7th/8th rank
2. Control of the centre of the board
3. An open file on the K-side
4. Control of a long diagonal, e.g. a1 ... h8
5. Pawn majority on the wings or centre
6. Cramping effect of the pawn formation
7. Backward pawn on a half-open file
8. Power of a passed pawn
9. Weak squares in the enemy position.

Each of these situations can be identified by the presence of certain values in the matrix Λ, depending of course on the precise choice of Γ'.

The relation Λ', suitably sliced by an appeal to the $(N+2)$-level, gives rise to two structures,

$K_{W'}(S')$, White's positional view of board, and

$K_{S'}(W')$, board's positional view of White.

In $K_{W'}(S')$ it is interesting to note that, since some of the s_j can vary throughout the course of a game, there are lower bounds for the maximum dimensions of the w_i, as follows:

w_1	(K)	13	w_4	(Q+B)	6
w_2	(Q)	4	w_5	(Q+B)	6
w_3	(Q+RS)	8	w_6	(NS)	29

This means that, at the positional level of play, the roles of the king and the knights are more complicated than are those for the other pieces. This probably reflects the action of the king in endgames and that of the knights in the middle game.

At the $(N+2)$-level of super-positional play we need a set W'' whose members are subsets of W' as well as a set S'' whose members are subsets of S'. We do not in fact insist that S'' be a cover of S', although it will effectively be a cover of S. The definition of Σ, in terms of Λ, must be such that it contains enough information for dealing with typical super-positional questions, such as the following:

1. What positional, $(N+1)$, features must be used in opening play?
2. Does the position justify a K-side attack?

3. Does the position justify material sacrifice?
4. Should White attack or defend?
5. What are the positional strengths/weaknesses in any mode?

It is an intriguing question to consider whether or not material loss/gain is really an $(N+3)$-matter, since 'material' is a word which covers 'all the pieces' (that is, all the elements of W'').

We take the following sets W'', S''.

name of element of W''		subset of W'
v_1	king power	(w_1, w_8)
v_2	piece power	$(w_2, w_3, w_4, w_5, w_6)$
v_3	pawn power	(w_7, w_8, w_9, w_{10})

name of element of S''		subset of S'
t_1	K-side files	(s_{15}, s_{16}, s_{17})
t_2	K-side diagonals	(s_{36}, s_{37}, s_{38})
t_3	Q-side files	(s_{10}, s_{11}, s_{12})
t_4	Q-side diagonals	(s_{23}, s_{24}, s_{25})
t_5	centre control	$(s_1, s_{13}, s_{14}, s_{12}, s_{15}, s_{24}, s_{36})$
t_6	Black weak squares	(s_{51})

The definition of Σ, a weighted relation, is taken as follows:

(i) Σ has a matrix representation with entries Σ_{ij}

(ii) $(v_i, t_j) \in \Sigma$ if there exists some (α, β) such that $w_\alpha \in v_i$, $s_\beta \in t_j$ and $(w_\alpha, s_\beta) \in \Lambda$

(iii) If I is the index set $\{(\alpha, \beta)\}$ of all pairs found under (ii) then
$$\Sigma_{ij} = \underset{(\alpha, \beta) \in I}{\text{Sum}} \Lambda_{\alpha\beta}$$

HOW THE COMPUTER MUST THINK

An outline of the positional thinking, between the three levels, is given in the following game (Lasker *v.* Napier, Cambridge Springs 1904). The computer details and results of game analysis will be given in a later paper, written jointly by Atkin, Hartston and Witten.

level/relation		remarks on White's play	move
1	$N+2/\Sigma$	Consider *centre, files, diagonals, ranks* in the super-position prior to making first move.	
	$N+1/\Lambda$	Select *centre + files + diagonals* strategy.	
	N/Γ	Find move in Γ compatible with $(N+1)$ strategy.	1 e2–e4
		(Black's reply)	c7–c5
2	$N+2/\Sigma$	Test Black's reply against positional choices; *centre*, etc.	
	$N+1/\Lambda$	Black contests *centre + Q-file* and threatens on QB-*file* (this 'threat' is assessment of Black's $(N+1)$-play).	

level/relation	remarks on White's play	move
N/Γ	Select move in Γ to contest *centre* (best is N–f3?).	2 N–c3
	(Black's reply)	N–c6
3 $N+2/\Sigma$	Test Black's reply against opening positional strategy.	
$N+1/\Lambda$	Black controls d4 in *centre* and black squares in *centre* and in *diagonal*.	
N/Γ	Select move to contest control of d4 and e5 (black squares).	3 N–f3
	(Black's reply)	g7–g6
4 $N+2/\Sigma$	Test Black's reply *re* positional struggle.	
$N+1/\Lambda$	Black's reply is compatible with his positional strategy; contests *diagonal* on *centre* squares but *not* on *this* move. Proceed with White's positional *centre* strategy.	
N/Γ	Select move to control *centre* + Q-file.	4 d2–d4
	(Black's reply)	c5 × d4
5 $N+2/\Sigma$	Test Black's reply *re* material loss + position.	
$N+1/\Lambda$	Material loss tolerated/avoided in *centre* contest? Compare with recapture in strategy, open Q-*file* and removal of Black's P.	
N/Γ	Recapture.	5 N × d4
	(Black's reply)	B–g7
6 $N+2/\Sigma$	Test Black's reply *re* positional struggle.	
$N+1/\Lambda$	Black controls *diagonal* and *centre* d4. White's N on d4 is on *rank*-4 and positionally threatens *rank*-5; an $(N+1)$ plus.	
N/Γ	N on d4 threatened (material loss). Select move maintain or retreat N? Go back to $(N+1)$ for decision. Then select to maintain.	6 B–e3
	(Black's reply)	d7–d6
7 $N+2/\Sigma$	Black's reply introduces new positional feature of open *diagonal* for QB. This contests White's Q-diagonal.	
$N+1/\Lambda$	Contest *diagonal* of Black's QB, or play on *diagonal* of White's QB, or play on open Q-*file*.	
N/Γ	Test $(N+1)$-ideas by possible moves. Notice that Q–d2 is strong move under $(N+1)$, where it achieves two goals. Move selected by Lasker	

level/relation	*remarks on White's play*	*move*
	contests Black's diagonal of QB. Cycle back to $(N+2)$ to find effect of h2–h3.	7 h2–h3
$N+2/\Sigma$	Suggests opening K R-*file* for White + P-attack on K-side after Black castles K-side. Suggests select a new $(N+1)$ strategy as follows:	
$N+1/\Lambda$	P advance on K-side and open *files* for rooks.	
	(Black's reply)	7 ... N–f6
8 $N+2/\Sigma$	Black's reply does not alter control at $(N+1)$. Select new $(N+1)$ strategy for White (as above).	
$N+1/\Lambda$	K-side attack by P-advance.	
N/Γ	Select move compatible with above. Cycle back to $(N+2)$ for confirming tactics.	8 g2–g4
$N+2/\Sigma$	No comment.	
$N+1/\Lambda$	Compatible, plus constraint on Black's QB, plus threat to Black's K N on further advance.	
	(Black's reply)	8 ... 0–0
9 $N+2/\Sigma$	Black's reply co-operates with new strategy.	
$N+1/\Lambda$	Continue with K-side attack.	
N/Γ	Select P-move.	9 g4–g5
	(Black's reply)	N–e8
10 $N+2/\Sigma$	Black's reply surrenders contest in *centre* and so	
$N+1/\Lambda$	no change in $(N+1)$ strategy.	
N/Γ	Select move to open R-*file*.	10 h3–h4
	(Black's reply)	N–c7
11 $N+2/\Sigma$	Black's reply suggests a counter-attack in the *centre* by d6–d5 or e7–e5 (a standard positional strategy). Modify the $(N+1)$-play to combine K-side attack and *centre* control.	
$N+1/\Lambda$	Search at N-level for K-side moves and *centre* control.	
N/Γ	Select K-side P-move if possible.	11 f2–f4
	(Black's reply)	e7–e5
12 $N+2/\Sigma$	Material threat by Black. Go to N-level for possibilities.	
N/Γ	Possible moves to avoid material loss: f4 × d5, leads to d6 × d5 and	
$N+1/\Lambda$	control of Q-*file* by Black, reject;	

level/relation	remarks on White's play	move
N/Γ	N×c6, leads to b7×c6 and	
N+1/Λ	loss of N for K-side attack, reject;	
N/Γ	N(d4)–e2, protects P on f4 and	
N+1/Λ	brings N to K-side, supporting strategy.	
N/Γ	Select N(d4)–e2.	12 N(d4)–e2
	(Black's reply)	d6–d5

13   *N*+2/Σ   Black's reply consistent with his positional strategy of a *centre* counterattack, but he offers P (material gain for White). Go to *N*-level for possible replies.

N/Γ   e4×d5, gains a P, which is good at (*N*+2), but

N+1/Λ   opens K-*file*, reduces K-side attack, but

N/Γ   threatens d5×c6 winning N, forces N-move in reply. Can the black N on c6 move to K-side in defence of White's attack by N–e7? Test to find d5–d6 to win material (good at (*N*+2)).

N/Γ   Any other moves permit Black's d5–d4 with attack in *centre* reaching *rank*-4 and material threat. Chooses to exchange P.   13 e4×d5

           (Black's reply)   N–d4

14   *N*+2/Σ   Black's attack on *rank*-3, *rank*-2 and K B-*file*. Exchange for material gain?

N+1/Λ   Ignore Black's attack and continue with K-side attack?

N/Γ   Possible move N–g3 to reinforce attack at (*N*+1)?

N+1/Λ   Strategy to remove attack by simplifying and so

N/Γ   select exchange of N by N, save white B to counter Black's B on black diagonal.   14 N×d4

           (Black's reply)   N×d5

15   *N*+2/Σ   Material loss/gain situation; consider that Black threatens N×e3 which weakens White's (*N*+1) positional

N+1/Λ   play on the black squares. This suggests exchange by

N/Γ   N×d5 which

N+1/Λ   surrenders white *diagonal* to Black's Q with attack on White's KR. Go back to (*N*+2) and check that

level/relation	*remarks on White's play*	*move*
$N+2/\Sigma$	White's N is *en prise*; avoid this by	
N/Γ	f4×e5, loses B on e3, reject (via $(N+2)$)	
N/Γ	N(d4) to move and we then see that	
$N+1/\Lambda$	the black N is threatened on the open Q-*file* so can the white N move to defend the B on e3?	
N/Γ	Possible move is N–f5?	
$N+1/\Lambda$	This furthers the K-side attack, no material loss.	15 N–f5
	(Black's reply)	N×c3
16 $N+2/\Sigma$	Black's reply is attempt to force material gain by loss of N on f5, but	
$N+1/\Lambda$	is there a check by N-move first?	
N/Γ	Select move which allows check.	16 Q×d8
	(Black's reply)	R×d8
17 N/Γ	Check black K by N move.	17 N–e7+
	(Black's reply)	K–h8
18 $N+2/\Sigma$	Material even, continue with positional K-side attack.	
$N+1/\Lambda$	Advance pawn to open *file*.	
N/Γ	Select P on h4.	18 h4–h5
	(Black's reply)	R–e8
19 $N+2/\Sigma$	Black threatens N and K-*file* (after a possible e5×f4), save material by (?)	
$N+1/\Lambda$	N×c8; this gains control of White diagonal on K-side for White; but it removes attacking piece from K-side; maintain N if possible.	
N/Γ	White's B can maintain N.	19 B–c5
	(Black's reply)	g6×h5
20 $N+1/\Lambda$	Open *file*, *diagonal*, increase attack	
N/Γ	R×h5 does not open *file* immediately B-move to threaten K-side.	20 B–c4
	(Black's reply)	e5×f4
21 $N+1/\Lambda$	Black has pinned the white N on the open K-*file* but failed to contest attack by the white K B.	
N/Γ	B×f7 wins material and	
$N+1/\Lambda$	reduces attack on the K-file.	21 B×f7
	(Black's reply)	N–e4
22 $N+2/\Sigma$	Black threatens material gain of B and so	
$N+1/\Lambda$	make White's N on e7 unprotected.	
$N+1/\Lambda$	Material gain to free N by B×e8?	
N/Γ	Select B×e8 and if then Black plays N×c5 White can proceed with	

level/relation	*remarks on White's play*	*move*
	R×h5.	22 B×e8
	(Black's reply)	B×b2
23 $N+2/\Sigma$	Black tries to equalise material.	
N/Γ	Avoid loss of QR by	23 R–b1
	(Black's reply)	B–c3
24 $N+1/\Lambda$	K move to square which is not on diagonal accessible to Black's QB on next move.	
N/Γ	Only one such square.	24 K–f1
	(Black's reply)	B–g4
25 $N+2/\Sigma$	Black's reply attempts to close R-*file* and to increase attack on squares near to the white K.	
$N+1/\Lambda$	Continue the K-side attack and open the K R-*file* if possible by countering Black's last move.	
N/Γ	Select B move on white diagonal.	25 B×h5
	(Black's reply)	B×h5
26 $N+2/\Sigma$	Avoid material loss and	
$N+1/\Lambda$	introduce R in R-*file*.	26 R×h5
	(Black's reply)	N–g3+
27 N/Γ	White K must move.	
$N+1/\Lambda$	Select a white square for best safety.	27 K–g2
	(Black's reply)	N×h5
28 $N+2/\Sigma$	The K-side attack is without its R. Look for a Q-side R attack on	
$N+1/\Lambda$	the open QN-*file* and then on *rank*-7.	
N/Γ	Material gain by R move.	28 R×b7
	(Black's reply)	a7–a5
29 $N+2/\Sigma$	Bring the QR to K-side for the attack. Black's most important defence is on the black diagonal a1–h8.	
$N+1/\Lambda$	Search for moves to get QR on K R-*file*.	
N/Γ	Threaten Black's B as cover for move to K-side.	29 R–b3
	(Black's reply)	B–g7

30   The game now proceeded by

      30   R–h3   N–g3
      31   K–f3   R–a6
      32   K×f4   N–e2+
      33   K–f5   N–c3
      34   a2–a3   N–a4
      35   B–e3   Resigns.

     There are many ways of translating this hierarchical procedure into a precise computer program. At the time of writing (March 1975) some of these ways are being explored and evaluated by a study of illustrative games of chess. But the process in each case can be described in the following way (figure 3):

(i) Rank the t_i-values in Σ by column sums.   (an $(N+2)$-decision)

(ii) Select the first ranking t_i-value, $(t_i)_1$.

(iii) Descend to Λ to unwrap the $(t_i)_1 = \bigcup_i s_j$ (an $(N+1)$-decision) and so to identify the pieces W_i on $S_k \in s_j$.
(This restricts the examination to certain pieces and certain squares of the board, identifying the sets I_j required by PEP.)

(iv) Define a map $J: W(\Gamma) \to W(\Gamma')$ which   (*N*-decisions) selects moves in Γ compatible with the selection made in (iii), for example,

(a) to decrease $|\dim W_i(\Gamma') - \dim W_i(\Gamma)|$

(b) to increase stval (S_k), for appropriate S_k

(c) to decrease $|\text{cval } W_i(\Gamma') - \text{cval } W_i(\Gamma)|$.

This provides parameter sets F, G, H at a depth of 1-ply.

(v) Now go to PEP and through the generated values PV select the best positional move for White.

(vi) Move to second ranking level in (i) and cycle round. This gives a total of two (positional) *candidate moves* for White.

(vii) With this process which generates candidate moves it is now feasible to enter a tree-searching mode. Because the tree of moves has been drastically pruned the depth of search can be made very much larger than usual.

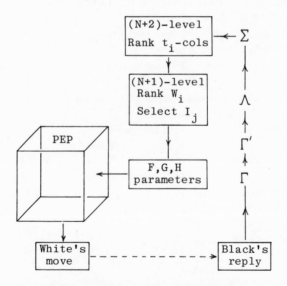

Figure 3. Hierarchical (positional) flow chart

ACKNOWLEDGEMENTS

The work described in this paper is the basis of a current research project at the University of Essex entitled 'Computer Simulation of Positional Play in Chess'. The author is indebted to the Science Research Council, who finance the project, and to his research colleagues I. H. Witten and W. R. Hartston.

REFERENCES

Atkin, R. H. (1972) Multidimensional structure in the game of chess. *Int. J. Man-Machine Studies 4*, 341–62.

Atkin, R. H. & I. Witten (1973) Mathematical relations in chess, in *Computer Chess*, Science Research Council, Atlas Computer Laboratory.

Atkin, R. H. (1975) An approach to structure in architectural and urban design, 3. Illustrative examples. *Environment and Planning B, 1.*

Describing Pawn Structures

S. T. Tan

THE THEORY OF GAMES

Few people would be surprised by the fact that the Borel-von Neumann theory of games as it is today, although originally intended to model parlour games, has little beyond terminological trivialities in common with computer chess. The reduction of extensive forms of zero-sum, two-person games with perfect information to their normalized forms by means of pure strategies (see e.g. Kuhn 1953) leads to a combinatorial explosion that puts even tic-tac-toe out of reach of game theory. In practice, what people do is to assume the normalized form in the first place, and the availability of utility functions. This makes the theory inapplicable to cases where we cannot find a small set of pure strategies, where the utilities cannot be obtained, or where statistical solutions in terms of mixed strategies are of no interest to us.

Nevertheless the transformation from extensive to normalized forms is conceptually significant; thinking in terms of strategies instead of moves is a step 'upwards', and the resulting matrix format is simpler and so more amenable to mathematical treatment than the tree format. Note that the normalized form is complete in itself, in the sense that once it is constructed, no reference to the original extensive form is needed.

Being less ambitious, one may then ask if it is not possible, by dropping the completeness property, to perform similar 'semantic ascents' which will be more useful in the case of chess and endgames in particular. This is attempted here for pawn endings: attack-defence dependency relations for groups of pawns and kings are used to express some general properties of the endings. However, before we go any further into the matter, lest anybody should think that we are equating any 'semantic ascent' with progress itself, we must first give reasons why such a step is not only desirable but also necessary.

REQUIREMENTS AND PRINCIPLES

The advantages of making requirements that we would like to see satisfied in intelligent chess programs, and the underlying principles, explicit are: it facilitates their debugging and it allows comparison with the actual realization, thus saving us from many illusions.

Plurality and Modularity

Plurality is here used as the opposite of uniformity, and is characterized by its ability to accommodate many special methods and special knowledge. It has been conjectured that intelligence is a question of having a 'big switch' (see e.g. Newell 1973, p. 10) that efficiently connects particular domains with special methods, each method representing expertise in its own domain.

Chess in general and endgames in particular may be viewed as one problem, and one may devise a uniform method to deal with it; or, alternatively, it may be considered as a mosaic of thousands of sub-problems, each requiring a different way of handling. Just think how nicely structured into stages is the mating process with a single rook; how king, knight and bishop coordinate to set mate; how one works backward from critical positions to find related squares in blocked or almost blocked pawn endings; how one takes advantage of previous exhaustive analysis in the form of Troitzky line, Baehr zones, the zones for Q vs P, etc.

The objection to uniformity is its inefficiency. Take static evaluation functions: if they are to be precise they must be sufficiently complex and costly, for, as examples demonstrate, minor perturbations in a position may easily alter the value or even the character of the position; if they are cheap then in general it is necessary to compensate their imprecision with extensive search. Besides, many evaluation functions are costly and imprecise, and ordinary pruning and termination heuristics are more suitable when search is extensive, which is why the second alternative is the more favoured one at present, as shown by recent tournament results. Only in special cases do we have evaluation functions which are simple and good at the same time. The same is true with regard to other forms of uniformity.

With the existence of thousands of expert programs, the role of the 'big switch' is of utmost importance, for it diagnoses and decides when to call which expert. It can become very complicated, because the diagnosis itself often depends on the results of the expert programs (lookahead). It is therefore desirable to have as much modularity as possible; modules should only depend on the results of the sub-modules, not on how they are obtained.

The next requirement is closely connected to the first, in fact its satisfaction is a prerequisite for the first.

Epistemological Adequacy

A representation is said to be epistemologically adequate for a person or machine (McCarthy and Hayes 1969) 'if it can be used practically to express the facts that one actually has about the aspects (of interest to the person or machine) of the world'. What we want is a chess program that is epistemologically adequate for us, so that we can express some of our chess knowledge and communicate it to the program. (It is our knowledge put in the machine; the controversy about what the machine actually knows is irrelevant here, for the moment at any rate.)

It is very fashionable today to talk of 'advising' a program, but often it consists of advice like: 'play Petroff, subtract 50 points', 'move light pieces from the back rank in the opening, reward 25 points', etc. This is advising the program on what we do not know (why not 26.75 points?).

If a chess master does a similar job or fiddles with parameters then he is wasting his talents; besides, there is enough of what we *do* know about chess that may be communicated by gradually building up the program's descriptional tools. It is not a question of simulating human thought: we do not require anywhere that the machine has the same thought processes as ours.

Satisfaction of this requirement would have the benevolent side-effect of making other important communications possible: the program's internal communications between moves ('continuity'), between branches of the analysis-tree (allowing elimination of redundant sub-analysis), between the expert programs (sharing of data), etc. The consequences are: possibility of a direct connection between board features and actions without having to go through the ritual of reducing everything to a number and then producing moves back from the numbers; creation of conditions for analogical reasoning; learning; etc. This is what we believe will, in the long run, tell on the playing performance of the program.

Past and Present

We hardly need to say that the requirements of the last section can only be realized step-wise and that we are still very far from the final state. Initially, we studied the feasibility of the approach, without too much concern with optimization, by actually writing the programs or sub-programs in detail to get the feel of their bulk.

In the single pawn case (Tan 1972) we concentrated on rules in the form of associations between predicates and action-schemes, how they combine to form decision trees, and how they are made independent from the actual evaluations and executions of the predicates and action-schemes. Recursive predicates representing lookaheads are not distinguished from others, and particular predicates associated with critical squares were dealt with.

In the bishop vs pawn program (Tan 1974a) predicates representing properties of a long-range piece, and the use of constraints and goals within action-schemes, were studied. But the main concern there was with the dichotomy of evaluation vs look-up and updating, deciding which predicates to evaluate and which to look up, and with the use of transition networks in the updating.

The case of rook vs bishop is used (Tan 1975) to study how examples from a book may be used when similar situations occur on the board. It assumes that the moves in the examples are interpreted, i.e. not only the moves but the action-schemes are given.

The basic ideas are:

1. Obvious moves should be handled separately by rules similar to those used in earlier works, so as not to burden the proper program for analogy.

2. Similarity is based on matching of descriptions of positions, but this alone (called 'surface matching') is never sufficiently reliable without

the accompanying verification or refutation ('deep matching') in the analysis. Matching and analysis thus become recursively intertwined. Particular heuristics relying on the partial ordering of moves of an action-scheme, which arises naturally when they are generated via goals and constraints, are suggested for this verification/refutation process.

The object of the present work is the description of general pawn-endings. Pawn structures decompose naturally into fronts and islands: no front has a direct influence on another and so each can be analysed separately. Kings are more mobile: not being tied to any particular locality, they can be used to attack or block enemy pawns, to support one's own pawns or else be used to manoeuvre or out-manoeuvre the opponent's king. They will not in general be able to fulfil all their possible tasks simultaneously, so the problem of distribution of effort will arise, as always when there is scarcity of active resources.

Particular problems are referred to as local problems (e.g. with respect to a particular front: can one breakthrough, sneakthrough, prevent breakthrough, who can lose tempo, or can the king stop one, two, or three pawns, etc.). These problems may be solved by means of established rules or, if these are not available, by analyses, which will be called partial analyses since they do not include all the pieces on board. Unlike our previous work, we will not bother with these local problems: we will assume that their answers are available, e.g. by writing the program interactively and providing it with 'oracles'.

With this assumption, the program's task is to make a general assessment of a general pawn-ending (i.e. to represent local threats and how strong they are, possible defences, if a king is overloaded, etc.) such that more global properties may be computed from them: e.g. if it is likely to be a race with a photo-finish (in which case Q vs Q, Q vs P, stale-mate, queening with check, etc., may be relevant), or if it is a position where careful manoeuvring with the kings is necessary (in which case use the method of related squares, see Averbakh and Maiselis 1960), etc. Note that the method of related squares belongs to analysis proper and is outside our scope. We must only establish when, not how, to use it.

This decomposition of the original problem into general assessment and analysis (local and global) is not entirely unrelated to practice. Kotov (1972), for example, finds it ideal to make general considerations when the opponent's clock is going, and to go through concrete analysis when his own clock ticks, excluding, of course, time trouble and extreme tactical situations.

In a complete playing program such a general assessment will be preceded by an orientation phase, where preliminary classification, usually based on material count, is made and on which basis it is decided whether it is necessary to make a general assessment at all (e.g. it is superfluous in the single pawn case). The general assessment may also be called an exploration phase, before the actual investigation and verification phases take place (for these phases, see de Groot 1965); and it is not wrong to say that one of the purposes of having descriptions is to enable

results of explorations (= partial analyses) to be expressed in a convenient way for use in further analysis, thus making stepwise analysis
possible. It follows that these descriptions must reflect the particularities
of the pawn structure, i.e. its decomposition into fronts and islands, their
relations to one another, and the relations between the kings and these
groups of pawns. This leads us to another use of the descriptions, to
localize the effects of a move. A pawn move belonging to front number 1
may affect its relations to enemy pawns in the same front and the kings,
but certainly not its relations to other fronts. It will then be relatively
easy to determine which previous partial analyses are still valid and which
are no longer so. (Compare the 'method of analogies' of KAISSA, see
e.g. Tan 1974b, which depends on complicated calculations of sets of
influence to determine if previous refutations are applicable in similar
situations.)

THE 9 × 10 + 1 BOARD

A complete representation of a situation in chess can be made very
simply: all the positions of the pieces, who is to move, and a little bit of
history (*en passant*, castling rights, repetition and the 50-move rule).
Such a 'first-order description' presents no problems, nevertheless it
should be made as efficient as possible, because many computations
depend on it. When there are only a few pieces on the board, two-
dimensional coordinates may be used; for general positions the 12 × 10
cylinder representation (see e.g. Kozdrowicki and Cooper 1973) is
popular, for it has the virtue of combining the two tests, 'is square x
outside the board?' and 'is square x occupied?', into one when generating
moves. An alternative is to keep the 8 × 8 board and to use tables for
generating moves (see Bell 1972).

The cylinder representation is adopted here, and with only pawns
and kings it becomes a 9 × 10 + 1 board (the last square is needed because

```
81  82  83  84  85  86  87  88  89  90
   +----------------------------------+
72 | 73  74  75  76  77  78  79  80   |
   |                                  |
63 | 64  65  66  67  68  69  70  71   |
   |                                  |
54 | 55  56  57  58  59  60  61  62   |
   |                                  |
45 | 46  47  48  49  50  51  52  53   |
   |                                  |
36 | 37  38  39  40  41  42  43  44   |
   |                                  |
27 | 28  29  30  31  32  33  34  35   |
   |                                  |
18 | 19  20  21  22  23  24  25  26   |
   |                                  |
 9 | 10  11  12  13  14  15  16  17   |
   +----------------------------------+
 0   1   2   3   4   5   6   7   8
```

Figure 1. The 9 × 10 + 1 board

of the slight twist of the cylinder): see figure 1. Conversions to two-dimensional coordinates and vice-versa may be easily done by:

$\text{FILE}(X) = X \text{ MOD } 9$

$\text{RANK}(X) = X \text{ DIV } 9$

$X = 9 * \text{RANK}(X) + \text{FILE}(X)$

where DIV is arithmetic division, and MOD gives the remainder. To generate all king moves, add (anti-clockwise) $-10, -9, -8, +1, +10, +9, +8,$ and $-1. +9$ and $+18$ are the one- and two-step pawn moves, $+8, +10, -8$ and -10 represent captures.

A position is given by the positions of WK, BK, number of white pawns, list of positions of white pawns, number of black pawns, and a list of positions of black pawns. For example,

32

51

3 (47 39 49)

4 (64 56 41 34)

represents the position shown in figure 2.

Figure 2. Keres-Alekhine, Dresden 1936, A361

The material count is used for preliminary classification, which determines what further refinement may be needed. In Averbakh and Maiselis (1960), for instance, the preliminary classification consists of: 1 vs 0, 1 vs 1, 2 vs 1, 2 vs 2, 3 vs 2 or 3, others. As explained in the last section, our concern here is mostly with the 'others' case.

PAWN TO PAWN RELATIONS

The terminology used in the following will, with some minor modifications, be that of Kmoch (1964). We restrict ourselves to binary pawn-to-pawn relations, since these are sufficient for our purposes, and they result in a coloured graph for which utility functions are more easily defined than if it were a general algebra or a relational structure.

An enemy pawn ahead on the same file is a *counterpawn*, and it is a *sentry* when it is on a neighbouring file. The definitions are not valid when the pawns have bypassed each other, and we will omit *en passant* to simplify matters. Counterpawns and mutual sentries of distance 1 are called *rams* and *levers* respectively. Friendly relations give rise to a *duo* when the pawns are abreast on two neighbouring files, and a *twin* (doublepawn) when they are on the same file. A backward neighbour is a *protector* (distance 1) or a *potential protector* (distance >1). All the above relations are irreflexive and intransitive, and all except those corresponding to the last three are symmetric. Two pawns are said to have no relations if none of the above hold. A summary of all relations is shown in table 1.

Table 1.

	name	graphical notation	code
hostile relations:	counterpawn	$< - >$	1
	ram	$< + >$	2
	sentry	$< .. >$	3
	lever	$< . + . >$	4
friendly relations:	duo	$=$	5
	twin	$= \times$	6 (inverse: 7)
	potential protector	$= >$	8 (inverse: 9)
	protector	$= / = >$	10 (inverse: 11)

(Note: $x = \times y$, $x = > y$, $x = / = > y$, if y is ahead of x.)

The resulting graph will be called a *pawn-relations graph* (PR-graph). The inverse relations for the three asymmetric relations will always be available although not explicitly drawn in the graph (in the actual machine representation the arrows are not physical pointers, and they may be traversed in both directions). For example, the graph of the position shown in figure 3 is shown in figure 4.

Figure 3. Euwe-Alekhine, 1935, A382

In the internal representation all relations of node 33 are stored within the node. It becomes:
$+ 33 (3,59) (3,70) (5,34) (7,24)$
($+$ for white, $3 =$ code for sentry, etc.) and the whole graph can then be embedded into the representation of the board.

Each connected component of the PR-graph is called a *front*, each connected component of the sub-graph formed by friendly relations is an *island*. In the above example there are two fronts, the king-side front consisting of one white and two black islands.

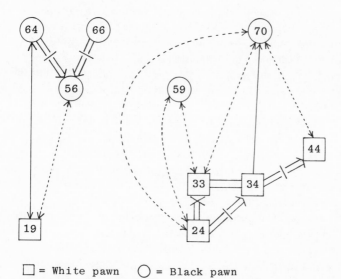

□ = White pawn   ○ = Black pawn

Figure 4. The pawn-relations graph for the position shown in figure 3

Apart from the decomposition into fronts and islands, the main use of the PR-graph is to facilitate detection of other important properties of pawn structures. A pawn with counterpawns(s) is either *unfree* (or blocked); *half-free*, if it has one or more sentries of distance >1; or else *free* (a *passer*). Note that a passer, as defined here, may have a sentry with which it forms a lever, and may be captured if the opponent has the move. Otherwise it may become a real passer by capturing its sentry or bypassing it. In such cases, the lever represents a critical transitional phase.

THE ATTACK-DEFENCE DIAGRAM (ADD)

As indicated at the end of the last section, levers may require special attention because of their unstable nature. Generally, there are points of contact with the enemy, e.g. a check or a king threatening to capture a pawn in one move, which need more or less urgent measures. Thus a check must be lifted immediately, and this has the power to interrupt or overrule any other rule.

On the other hand, we would like to see in a higher order description of a position those features that have a more permanent character, since this is the property which forms the basis of the rationale of communicating information from one node to another in the analysis-tree. We decided therefore to exclude immediate points of contact from the descriptions considered below.

A passer represents a threat, and the nearer to promotion the stronger the threat. An unfree or a half-free pawn, if it can be converted to a passer, is also a threat. The conversion may take place simply by pushing forward with a friendly neighbour helping a candidate, the neighbour in turn supported by the helper's helper, etc., by deflection of a sentry or a counterpawn (sometimes using the fork lever trick) or by a combination of both. These methods of forcing passers apply to a front, independent of the number of the islands and neglecting the kings.

Sometimes, both sides can force passers (mutual breakthrough); sometimes only one side can force a passer, and it can do so without giving the other side passers (pure breakthrough); or it can do so only by letting enemy pawns pass (we refer to this last case as sneaking: the terminology is open to suggestions here). Threats represented by passers and pure breakthroughs are denoted by $=>$ (notation not to be confused with those for the PR-graph). A mutual breakthrough consists of two threats in opposite directions ($<=>$), and sneaking is a threat with a conditional counter-threat ($<::=>$).

Threats may be reduced or neutralized by self-defence of the pawns of the inferior side, e.g. by blocking the position, or else they may be met by the opponent's king. Self-defence by pawns will not be represented explicitly, but 'defence' (denoted by $->$) will be used to refer to relations of kings and threats. Other forms of threats (also represented by $=>$) are capture of pawns(s) by a king, support of an advance of pawns by a king, and the joint attack of king and pawns against the other side's pawns (e.g. dispersion via exchanges or sacrifices then capture).

A syntax of the attack-defence relations can be given in BNF as follows (* and % applied to a syntax class indicate the number of occurrences that the syntax class may have: for * it is one or more, for % it is one or zero):

```
(1)   <ADD>::=<REL*>
(2)   <REL>::=<A-REL>/<D-REL>/<B-REL>
(3)   <A-REL>::=<ACTOR><ACTOR%><A-LINK><ACTOR>
(4)   <D-REL>::=<ACTOR><D-LINK><A-REL>
(5)   <B-REL>::=<GROUP><B-LINK><GROUP>
(6)   <ACTOR>::=<KING>/<GROUP>
(7)   <A-LINK>::=<A-LINKTYPE><PAR><MOD%><DL%>
(8)   <D-LINK>::=<D-LINKTYPE><PAR><MOD%><D_%>
(9)   <B-LINK>::=<B-LINKTYPE><PAR%><MOD%><DL%>
(10)  <KING>::=K <COLOUR><LOC><DL%>
(11)  <GROUP>::=P <COLOUR><DL>/NIL
(12)  <A-LINKTYPE>::= => / <=> / <::=>
(13)  <D-LINKTYPE>::= ->
(14)  <B-LINKTYPE>::= [=] / = / [=
(15)  <COLOUR>::=WHITE/BLACK
(16)  <LOC>::=10/11............./80
```

An attack-defence diagram (ADD) is a set of instances of relations (1). (The operation of concatenation in the syntax does not commit us to any particular machine representation. In (1) it may be considered as set-theoretic union.)

REL is an instance of a relation, which may be of attacking, defensive or balanced type (2). Attacking and defensive relations were considered above; the first may have up to two active actors and one passive actor (3).

When no breakthroughs or sneakings can occur, the pawns are said to be *balanced*: they may be completely blocked, semi-blocked or blocked on one side (14).

A group (11) is a group of islands of pawns of the same colour belonging to one front. The special case with no pawns at all (all the pawns of the other side are passers) is denoted by the dummy NIL.

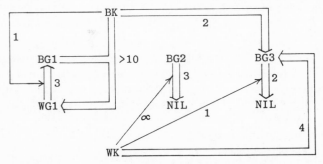

Figure 5. The ADD for the position shown in figure 2

It is sometimes convenient to think of an ADD as a generalized graph (some A-links have binary input), with actors as nodes and links and edges (see figure 5). Each node and link may have additional information attached to them: COLOUR; LOC(ation); PAR(ameter), indicating strengths of threats, etc.; MOD(ifier), indicating negation; modalities (possible, impossible, etc.; this facility is not used at the moment); and DL (description list) which may contain all sorts of things. Thus a DL of an A-link may contain the variations that lead to breakthroughs or, in the case of an attack of a king against a pawn group, the path(s) of the king to its target: a DL of a D-link can give the area to which a king is confined (referred to as binding) if it is to check the advance of a particular group: a DL of a king node can be used to combine the different bindings that the king suffers in meeting different threats, so allowing detection of overloading: a DL of a group indicates the number of pawn islands in the group, their location and numerical strength, particular interesting pawns (passers, potential targets, etc.).

Not all ADDS constructed according to the above syntax are permissible. There are additional semantic rules, for example if a threat of a breakthrough by a white group WG1 against a black group BG1 cannot be met by the black king, then there can be no question of a joint attack of BK and BG1 against WG1. Also, if the WK is immobilized by black threats, it will not think of attacking faraway black pawn groups. In the case of support of pawns by the king, the pawns must already be able to break or sneak through by themselves in order to get support.

We need not, however, bother with all these rules, syntactic or semantic; we are not considering whether some arbitrary structure is a permissible, well-formed ADD, we are only interested in ADDS constructed from legal pawn endings.

CONSTRUCTION AND USE

Let us now consider the construction of ADDs of positions in greater detail. Suppose that figure 2 is the input position. From the PR-graph, the algorithm CONSADD receives data on the different components of the graph. These define the nodes of the ADD:

BK(51)   WK(32)
BG1(64, 56)   WG1(47 39 49)
BG2(39)
BG3(49)

(we omit most of the information in the description lists). CONSADD now starts asking the local sub-programs (or the oracle in our case) questions about different relations between these nodes. Because of the semantic rules, the sequence of questions matters; CONSADD uses the following sequence:

1. Relations within fronts,
2. Defences to threats of (1),
3. Possible attacks of kings against pawns,
4. Defences to (3),
5. Support possibilities,
6. Joint attacks.

1. This produces: $WG1 => BG1$, $BG2 => NIL$, $BG3 => NIL$, each with the associated estimates of the minimal number of moves (PAR) necessary for the successful execution of the threat (always assuming that the superior side has the move).

2. BK can meet the threat $WG1 => BG1$, but only just. If White moves first then BK must immediately react to it, in other words, Black can afford to pass just once, i.e. giving White the move. Hence $PAR = 1$.

In general: $PAR = N > 0$ means 'can pass N times and still meet the threat'; $PAR = 0$ means 'must move immediately to meet threat'; and $PAR = -N < 0$ means 'must move first, and then would still need N moves to meet the threat'. In the example, if BK had been at G4 PAR would be 0, and if at H2, $PAR = -2$. When the king is directly in front of a passer or a candidate we make exceptions to the above: $PAR = \infty$ if the king is immediately in front of it, or else $PAR = M$ (large number).

Similarly WK can meet the threats $BG2 => NIL$ and $BG3 => NIL$. Each of these defences implies bindings on the king, e.g. $WK -> (BG3 => NIL)$ confines WK to H1, H3, G1, G2, F1, F3, E1, E2, and E3 (F3 is included because we had only taken G3 and WK into account).

Before continuing with 3, CONSADD looks for combined threats and their associated bindings. This is usually just finding intersections of the old bindings, but sometimes it needs a little analysis, for example with WK on F1 and BG2 on E3 instead of E4, WK must stay on F1 and cannot move at all.

3. Attacks of WK on BG1 and BG2 are ruled out because of the bindings the WK has already received (actually this is done by comparing the reward it gets if the attack on the pawns is successful and the penalty

received by ignoring the bindings). Attack of BK on WG1 is also ruled out, so there is only the attack WK $= >$ BG3, with PAR $= 4$ (number of moves up to capture) and the path E2, F1, G2, G3 is stored in the description list.

4. The path E2, F1, G2, G3 does not cross any square controlled by BK, so no defence offered.

5. To support the advance of pawns the king must find a square immediately in front of a passer or a candidate. The only possible supporting action here is BK $= >$ BG3, with PAR $= 2$ (number of moves up to control of G2), DL:path $=$ G4, H3.

6. The only joint attack possible is that of BK & BG1 $= >$ WG1. It takes >10 moves (BK goes to B7, then A6, etc.).

The ADD of the position is now complete (figure 5). It is then passed to the program DIAGADD which diagnoses the position and provides interface with the proper analysis. DIAGADD will try to see if the position is: (a) balanced or not, or if it is greatly imbalanced, in which case it may suggest to analysis that it is an easy problem not requiring very deep analysis; and (b) dynamically or statically balanced. There are of course different degrees of dynamic balance: the strongest is where threat and counterthreat are of roughly the same strength with insufficient defences, and the most static one is where the position is completely or almost completely blocked. When the threats and counterthreats are about equal, it may suggest to analysis to watch for checks, to be prepared for queen endings, etc.

It also analyses compatibility of the different options open for the kings. In doing so, it may establish that apparently different tasks may actually be reconciled, and a useful multipurpose move will then be suggested to analysis (see e.g. Reti's study, 1921, A71).

In the example, it would find that BK $- >$ (WG1 $= >$ BG1) is compatible to BK and BG1 $= >$ WG1 (the path E5, D6, C7, B7 is within the binding of the first), but that both are incompatible with BK $= >$ BG2. It could thus present analysis with an alternative: either BK goes to the king-side or to the queen-side (both win, incidentally, Black to move; the first is the solution chosen by Alekhine in the game, the second discovered by Averbakh). Each alternative here decomposes the ADD into two connected components, enabling further simplification.

UPDATING AND CAUSALITY

It should be obvious from the previous section, that CONSADD is an expensive operation which cannot be applied to every position during the analysis. This is true even for the relatively simpler construction of the PR-graph. However, they were never intended to be so used, for the PR-graph and the ADD of a position are meant to contain information that is not expected to change rapidly from move to move, so that updating them will generally be a lot easier than reconstruction.

We refer to the collection of information, including ADD and the PR-graph, which are carried along from move to move with some updating, as the frame, in more or less the same sense as the 'frame' of the 'frame problem' (McCarthy and Hayes 1969, Hayes 1971). The original frame problem refers to the updating of an internal model of an external environment, but it makes no difference if we use it for a model of a model. The problem and its possible solutions have been discussed at length (e.g. Hayes 1971), and our concern here is not with the general problem but with the problem of choosing a representation for our particular domain, for which updating can be done as simply as possible. In particular we would like the blanket assumption (nothing changes unless explicitly stated) to be valid.

For the PR-graph, it is obvious that if pawn x advances, then x may change its relations to other pawns (old relations may disappear, new relations will never appear), but all other relations will remain the same. When x captures Y, the changes are slightly more complicated (new relations may appear), but still localized. The collection of all possible changes for each type of move can be represented by a *transition diagram* (see Tan 1976 for the use of the same for bishop to pawn relation). For example, the transition diagram for PUSH X (ONE STEP) is shown in figure 6, split into its five components.

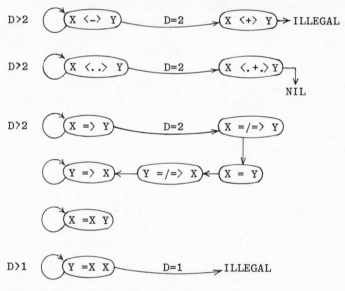

Figure 6. The transition diagram for PUSH X (ONE STEP)

Each transition has a condition that must be satisfied for the transition to take place, and these conditions refer to the state before the transition (D-distance). 'No condition' means transition under any condition, 'illegal' means illegal move under the conditions, 'nil' indicates disappearance of the relation (bypassing of pawns). The transition diagrams for PUSH X (TWO STEPS) and CAPTURE X Y may be given similarly.

The difficulty of updating arises from the propagation of changes: first there is the primary change, which causes secondary changes, which in turn produce tertiary changes, and so on. The PR-graph and the ADD are so constructed that they satisfy a 'no propagation law'. In the first case, this is simply because none of the pawn-to-pawn relations are transitive. In the case of the ADD, it can be seen as follows: excluding promotions and captures (sometimes causing disappearance of a whole pawn group), which need special treatment, we are left with 'ordinary' pawn and king moves.

A pawn move may reinforce or reduce (in case of self-defence) a threat, and in either case defences to the threat are clearly affected. Advancing a pawn may make its support more difficult, its logistic supply becomes strained, so to speak, and it may also become more or less vulnerable as a target for the enemy king.

For a king, movement in one direction will in general affect its influence in other directions. In addition, if it was a change in an attack vs pawns, it may change the defence by the other king.

These two causality laws for pawn and king moves must not be superimposed. If, for example, a pawn (belonging to BG1) move strengthens a joint attack by BG1 and BK against WG1, then this change in the joint attack will certainly not affect any other link emanating from BK. The second law may be applied only if the joint attack is changed by a BK move. This is typical of the intransitivity of changes of the ADD.

It would seem then that it contradicts Hayes' (1971) transitivity axiom for his causality relation, which was defined as $(a \rightarrow b)$iff ($\rightarrow$ here means 'causally related to'): if some property of b changes then some property of a is liable to change.

In fact the axiom can be reconciled with the above by carefully defining what the a and b are in our case: not the links of the ADD, but the parts of the links connected to its different actors are the units for which the causality relation should be defined. Thus the above pawn move is now said to change the pawn's part, but not the BK's part of the joint attack. The two parts are obviously not causally connected, although each of them may change shared common data (e.g. the PAR associated with the joint attack), and a change in one part looks exactly like a change in the other.

If we express the causality relations of the ADD in another (of still higher order) diagram, we see that this diagram decomposes into several disconnected components. So, while the transitivity axiom holds, we can keep the 'no propagation law', and everything comes to a happy ending.

ACKNOWLEDGEMENTS

This paper is part of a work on endgames supported by a grant from the Scientific Research Council. For various suggestions, criticisms and corrections we are indebted to Mr A. J. Roycroft.

References

Averbakh, J. & I. Maiselis (1960) *Lehrbuch der Endspiele* Vol. 1, *Bauern-endspiele*. Berlin.

Bell, A. G. (1972) *Games Playing with Computers*. London.

de Groot, A. (1965) *Thought and Choice in Chess*. The Hague.

Hayes, P. J. (1971) A logic of actions, in *Machine Intelligence 6* (eds. B. Meltzer & D. Michie), 495–520. Edinburgh.

Kmoch, H. (1964) *Pawn Power in Chess*. New York.

Kotov, A. (1972) *Think Like a Grandmaster*. London.

Kozdrowicki, E. W. & D. W. Cooper (1973) COKO III: The Cooper-Koz chess program, *CACM 16* (7), 411–26.

Kuhn, H. W. (1953) Extensive games and the problem of information, in *Contributions to the Theory of Games* (eds. H. W. Kuhn & A. W. Tucker) 193–216. Princeton.

McCarthy, J. & P. J. Hayes (1969) Some philosophical problems from the standpoint of artificial intelligence, in *Machine Intelligence 4* (eds. B. Meltzer & D. Michie) 463–502. Edinburgh.

Newell, A. (1973) Artificial intelligence and the concept of mind, in *Computer Models of Thought and Language* (eds. R. C. Shank & K. M. Colby) 1–60. San Francisco.

Tan, S. T. (1972) Representation of knowledge for very simple pawn endings in chess. *Research Memo MIP-R-98*, Department of Machine Intelligence, University of Edinburgh.

Tan, S. T. (1974a) Kings, pawn and bishop. *Research Memo MIP-R-108*, Department of Machine Intelligence, University of Edinburgh.

Tan, S. T. (1974b) The winning program (summary of some ideas of KAISSA), *Firbush News 5*, 38–40.

Tan, S. T. (1976) Rook vs bishop via book examples (in progress).

Tree-Searching and Tree-Pruning Techniques

J. A. Birmingham and P. Kent

This paper first discusses the now standard tree searching techniques of mini-max and alpha-beta and the recent improvements to alpha-beta, in particular the killer heuristic. It then describes a new and very powerful technique that we have termed 'razoring'. Unlike the alpha-beta technique, razoring cannot guarantee finding the optimum solution but it will, however, always find a good solution in a much shorter time. Typically a four-ply tree with a branching factor of 33 can be searched *an order of magnitude faster* than with alpha-beta. We also discuss 'forward marginal pruning'—a technique similar to razoring.

We then discuss 'chopper', a simple but usually overlooked device that avoids wasting time making a choice when no choice exists. Finally we consider a 'feed-over' technique to improve the effectiveness of alpha-beta and razoring.

MINI-MAX ALGORITHM

This technique (Shannon 1950, Turing 1953) is best described in terms of a game between Max and Min, where Max attempts to maximize the ultimate value of the game while Min attempts to minimize it. We will illustrate the technique by means of a simple game tree (figure 1), which has a branching factor of 3 and a depth of 2 ply. The square nodes indicate that it is Max's turn to move while the circles indicate that it is Min's turn. The nodes represent positions reached after a sequence of moves by Max and Min.

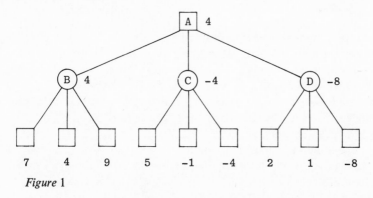

Figure 1

In the mini-max algorithm scores are only computed for the deepest level of the game tree, and are then 'backed up' to higher levels. No scores are computed for nodes at intermediate levels of the tree.

Min chooses the lowest score from her three choices at B, i.e. 4. She repeats this procedure for nodes C and D, obtaining values −4 and −8. Max then selects from the backed up values of B,C,D the node with the highest value; in this case B with a value of 4. The mini-max value of the tree is therefore 4 and Max's decision is to move to node B.

ALPHA-BETA TREE PRUNING ALGORITHM

The alpha-beta algorithm (Newell, Shaw and Simon 1959; Fuller, Gaschnig and Gillogly 1973) obtains exactly the same result as the mini-max algorithm, but is faster because it does not examine all the nodes of the tree.

We can again consider a game between Max and Min (figure 2). At node D it is Max's choice, so the value 4 is backed up to node D. The second node that Max finds from node E has value 5, the backed up value at node E is therefore $\geqslant 5$. As Min has a choice at node A of going to node D or node E, she will not select node E. There is therefore no point in examining the remaining successor nodes of E. This is an example of β-pruning.

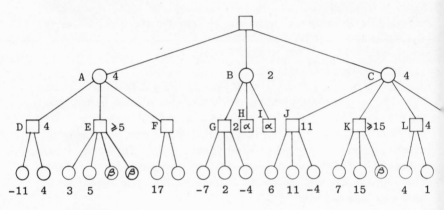

Figure 2

α-pruning is similar to β-pruning with the rules of minimizing and maximizing reversed. Thus Max has the initial choice of nodes A,B,C. He can obtain a score of 4 by going to node A. Min can limit Max to 2 or less at node B by selecting node G. Nodes H and I are therefore not worth examining and are cut by α-pruning. Similarly Min can limit the value at node C to 4 or less by choosing node L. The value of the tree is therefore 4 and Max's decision is to move to node A.

The mini-max algorithm would have obtained the same result as alpha-beta but would have required the evaluation of 28 nodes instead of 15.

Deep Alpha-Beta Pruning

An alpha or beta cut-off value may be used to prune trees at any node which is an even number of levels below it (Fuller, Gaschnig and

Gillogly 1973). This can be illustrated by the four-ply tree shown in figure 3.

In this example the value of α is obtained from the value backed up to node B, i.e. 7. As the first successor to node E has value 4 the remaining nodes are cut by deep α-pruning. A new value of 9 is found for α at node F. As the first successor to node G has the value 8 the remaining nodes are cut by shallow α-pruning. A similar technique may be used for deep β-pruning.

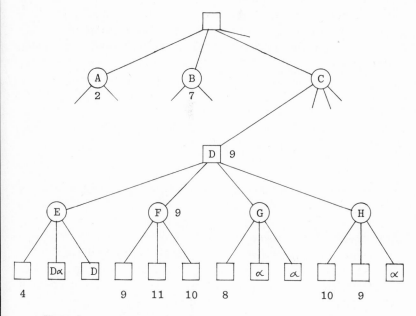

Figure 3

Killer Heuristic or Refutation

To analyze a four-ply tree with a branching factor of 33 the minimax algorithm will evaluate about one million bottom nodes. If the bottom nodes have a wide range of values and are randomly ordered the alpha-beta algorithm will reduce this number to about 25000.

A considerable improvement can be obtained by ordering the nodes at each level before applying the alpha-beta algorithm. Typically, mean branching factors can be reduced from 33 to 7 or 8 using the ordered alpha-beta technique.

A number of techniques have been used to perform this ordering, from fairly simple static ordering to elaborate dynamic systems. The simplest way is to make use of the same static evaluation function as used at the deepest level of the tree. One simply evaluates each node at a particular level and then sorts them into the appropriate order. However this technique cannot be used at the deepest level of the tree, as one has to evaluate all nodes before re-ordering, by which time it is too late to be of any use.

An alternative technique for ordering the moves is the killer heuristic (Gillogly 1972, Cichelli 1973, Bell 1973, Adelson-Velskiy *et al.* 1963). It can be used at all levels of the tree but is particularly useful at the deepest level where other methods cannot be used. It works on the principle that a move that refutes *one* of Max's moves is likely to refute the rest of Max's moves.

The way in which this is implemented will depend on the particular application. Care has to be taken that the overheads involved in the re-ordering do not outweigh the reduction in node evaluations. In our chess program the score for the best move of each piece is kept and used to select the order in which each piece is examined. This complete ordering of the pieces is performed each time that an alpha cut-off does not occur at the deepest level of the tree. A further ordering takes place whenever an alpha cut-off does occur. As this is much more frequent we only move the 'killer' piece to the head of the list of pieces and just shift the intervening pieces down one place.

This produced approximately a 50 per cent reduction in node evaluations and a 40 per cent reduction in time.

RAZORING

Occams Razor: One should not make an assumption unless there is a good reason to do so.

Inverse: If there is a very good reason to make an assumption then make it (even if it is not *always* true).

This technique works on the assumption that from any given position my opponent will be able to find at least one move that improves his position. This assumption is invalid in the context of chess if a *zugzwang* situation occurs. In fact the program defines *zugzwang* precisely as a state in which every move available to one player creates a position having a lower value to him (in its own evaluation terms) than the present board position.

Razoring is a new and very powerful technique for speeding up mini-max searching. Unlike alpha-beta it will not guarantee finding the best decision but it will, however, find a very good move far faster than alpha-beta. In an *n*-ply tree alpha-beta will prune plies 2 to *n*, while razoring will prune plies 1 to *n*–1. Razoring has frequently been observed to cut a list of 40–50 choices at ply 1 to a single node, while it once found the best choice in 28th position. Thus it is an effective way of automatically limiting the width of search at ply 1, and a considerable improvement on the rather arbitrary technique of picking the first *m* moves, a technique used in most current chess programs.

The program lists Max's three moves B,C,D (figure 4), makes each one in turn and computes a static evaluation for the resulting positions. The moves are ordered according to these values of 10, 8 and 2, and are then examined in order of decreasing value. The three replies to move B are valued 6,12,20. Min selects the lowest of these, so the backed up value at node B is 6.

Move C has static value 8 which is greater than 6, the value of Max at node A, and we therefore examine it further. The first reply has value 4, and all further replies to move C are therefore cut by α-pruning as the backed up value at node C must be $\leqslant 4$, which is < 6 (the value of α at node B).

Move D has a static value of 2. This is less than the present value of Max and will be even worse after Min has found her best reply (on the above assumption). We do not, therefore, examine this further; it has been razored out.

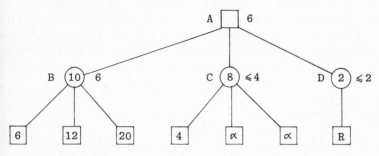

Figure 4

Deep Razoring

The razoring technique can be extended to cut deeper trees by comparing values backed up from, say, ply 4 of a four-ply program, with the static values at ply 1. This is risky, however, as it assumes that an improvement cannot be found (for me) by the sequence yourmove, mymove, yourmove. This is a weaker assumption than the normal one; that an improvement (for me) cannot result from yourmove.

In order to keep the tempo of the evaluation correct, plies 1 and 3 should be cut using the value backed up from the static evaluation at ply 4, while ply 2 should be cut using the value backed up from the static evaluation at ply 3.

Enhanced Razoring

In normal razoring, a node at plies 1 or 3 is cut if its static value is less than or equal to Max, where Max is the valued backed up from ply 4 to ply 1. A node is cut at ply 2 if its static value is less than or equal to Min (where Min is the value backed up from ply 3 to ply 1).

The degree of pruning can be modified by comparing the static node evaluations with Max or Min plus some value PRUNE. With a value of PRUNE = 30 the chess program plays a sound but unimaginative game taking level swaps at every opportunity. All the more subtle moves are cut out at ply 1. It averages about 500 node evaluations per move, i.e. about two seconds per move. In order to keep the subtle moves it has been found necessary to have different levels of enhancement at each ply. The present values are PRUNE1 = 0, PRUNE2 = 20, PRUNE3 = 40. This produces a similar standard of moves to the unenhanced razoring in about one-third of the time.

To put the prune values in context, a pawn is worth about 40 points.

MARGINAL FORWARD PRUNING

This technique (Slagle 1971) is similar to deep razoring with enhancement, and prunes by comparing the static value at any ply with the α-β value. One problem is that the tempo of the evaluation at the final ply is always wrong for one side or the other, but the effect of this can be reduced by putting an element of tempo in the evaluation function. For example, if a capture is made at the final ply of the search which leaves a piece *en prise*, then the value of the capture should be greatly reduced. For one side the basic assumption is the same as for deep razoring, i.e. I cannot improve my score by the sequence yourmove, mymove, yourmove. For the other side, however, the assumption is that you cannot improve your move by the sequence mymove, yourmove. This is an even weaker assumption than the one for deep razoring. It can be overcome by allowing for a margin of error, i.e. we examine all moves having a static value greater than α-ERROR.

The second problem with this technique is found also in deep razoring. Most of the time the static value and the backed up value for any position are reasonably similar and the pruning behaves in a fairly stable manner. On occasion however the static and backed up values differ by considerably more than the ERROR margin. This causes one side to be pruned very lightly and the other side extremely heavily, with disastrous consequences.

CHOPPER

When playing a game a chess playing program has to search a sequence of trees, and occasionally one of the trees in a given sequence will have a single node at ply 1. It is well worth while to test for such an occurrence, otherwise the program will search through plies 2,3,4, etc., only to decide that its only choice is also its best choice! So long as the value of the tree is not required, but only the decision about which move to select, one can chop the tree off at ply 1 and the only move available.

This situation often occurs in chess when the king has to move out of check.

FEED-OVER TECHNIQUE

In a chess program much effort is put into sorting moves into the best order at the various levels of the tree and then selecting replies to each of the moves. This transforms the initial randomly organised tree into a well-ordered tree having all the best sequences of moves in one part of the tree.

Once a move has been selected the whole tree is lost and then rebuilt two plies further on at the next move. As this seems very wasteful we now save the most important parts of the tree and use them to speed up the searching process on the next move. The optimum sequence from each of my opponent's possible replies to my chosen move is saved. This sequence is then fed back in after my opponent has responded and examined first. This primes alpha-beta with a good value at the start, and this can produce a considerable reduction in the number of nodes examined. The overhead for feed-over was found to be about 5 per cent, giving an average node reduction of approximately 30 per cent.

APPLICATION TO THE CHESS PROGRAM

Most of the better chess programs search to a 'Turing dead position'. This has been a standard technique for several years. We question this approach and instead attempt to compute a static evaluation for non-quiescent positions. In order to do this we have to have an element of lookahead in the evaluation function, achieved by giving values for threats to pieces as well as captures. We also include values for pins, x-rays, control of centre squares and squares near the kings. The value of threats by the player about to move is greater than that of the player who has just moved, producing an element of tempo in the evaluation function. By the use of tables we have also been able to give pieces different values in different positions on the board, for example knights are weak at the edges of the board and pawns increase in value as they advance.

The degree of pruning achieved is to some extent dependent upon the evaluation function. One can in fact use the node count to tune the evaluation, for if the node count goes very high on some move it is usually indicative that an important element is missing from the evaluation routine.

While our program could run into trouble evaluating long sequences of swaps, it gets compensation by examining the full width of moves, subject only to pruning by the various algorithms. This means that the program will often select quite subtle moves, which would be lost if a fixed width of search were used.

The actual move selected at ply 1 has been as low at 28th in the list. On another occasion the program found a knight fork of a king and queen first in the list at ply 1, checked it out to ply 4 and then razored out the remaining 40 or so moves without examining any of them deeper than ply 1. The razor technique seems able to cut the tree ruthlessly when there is an obvious sequence of moves, but to search far wider when the position is uncertain.

Initial experiments indicate that a four ply deep chess program with alpha-beta takes about 40 seconds per move using the optimized PL1 compiler on an IBM 370/165. With razoring the time falls to about twelve seconds and with enhanced razoring about four seconds, while most of the moves selected remain the same.

CONCLUSIONS

We have found that the razoring technique will cut about half the branches from each node left after alpha-beta pruning. We can therefore obtain *an order of magnitude improvement* in pruning a four-ply tree over ordered alpha-beta.

We have found no evidence to suggest that it is necessary to evaluate only at 'Turing dead positions'. In practice the program seems capable of handling quite turbulent positions.

The feed-over technique was found to be very useful and effective. It not only speeds up the search but also encourages the program to keep to a particular line instead of starting from scratch at each move.

The problem of the horizon effect has been observed only once in the last eight games played by the program. This problem occurs when a program throws away material to delay a strong move (e.g. a pawn queening) beyond the limit of its lookahead. The problem is obviously less likely to occur as the depth of search increases since the value of the material sacrificed will eventually be greater than the value of the pawn queening. The one case occurred in the game with R. Maybury at move 44 when the program sacrificed a knight to get a series of delaying checks. This put off a pawn queening to the 8th ply, i.e. beyond its horizon.

ACKNOWLEDGEMENTS
Many people have helped in 'educating' MASTER. In particular we would like to acknowledge Jack Howlett for providing the machine time, Alex Bell for convincing many people that what we were doing with the time was sensible, Chris Osland for running the program whilst we were otherwise occupied and John Waldron, its tutor in chess. Many other people gave up their Sunday afternoons to play the program, some of these are recorded in appendix 2.

Finally, we thank all those in the Harwell and Atlas/Rutherford Computing Divisions (particularly the operators and shift leaders who had every right to throw us out but, surprisingly, never did).

REFERENCES
Adelson-Velskiy, G.M., V.L.Arlazarov & A.G.Uskov (1966) Programme playing chess, in *Report on Symposium on Theory & Computing Methods in the Upper Mantle Problem.*

Bell, A.G. (1973) in *Computer Chess.* Proceedings of a one-day meeting on chess playing by computer, Atlas Computer Laboratory, Chilton, Didcot, Oxon, 1–13. SRC.

Cichelli, R.J. (1973) Research progress report in computer chess, *Sigart Newsl.* no. 41, 32–6.

Fuller, S.H., J.G.Gaschnig & J.J.Gillogly (1973) *Analysis of the alphabeta pruning algorithm.* Dept. of Computer Science, Carnegie-Mellon University, Pittsburgh, Pennsylvania.

Gillogly, J.J. (1972) The Technology chess program. *AI3*, 145–64. Also *Technical Report 71*, Carnegie-Mellon University, Pittsburgh, Pennsylvania.

Newell, A., J.C.Shaw & H.A.Simon (1959) Chess playing programs and the problem of complexity. *IBM J. 2*, 320–35. Also in E.A. Feigenbaum & J.A.Feldman (1963) *Computers and Thought.*

Shannon, C. E. (1950) Programming a computer for playing chess. *Phil. Mag. 41*, 256–75.

Slagle, J. R. (1971) *Artificial Intelligence: The Heuristic Programming Approach.* McGraw-Hill.

Turing, A. M. (1953) Digital computers applied to games, in *Faster than Thought* (ed. B. V. Bowden) 286–310. London: Pitman.

Appendix 1. The MASTER Program

THE BOOK

This consists of approximately 300 lines of ten moves for each side. The moves are considered in any order to allow for transpositions. The program frequently gets taken out of the book and then transposes back in. The main purpose of the book is to develop pieces in a reasonable order so that they do not block each other. It also saves computer time and helps to avoid opening traps.

The most favourable lines for White are placed at the top of the book and those favourable for Black at the bottom. When playing White the program scans the book from the top and when playing Black it scans from the bottom. To change the opening we merely have to change the first or last line in the book.

THE EVALUATION FUNCTION

Parameters are only included in the evaluation function if they are cheap to compute and necessary, i.e. they either produce a very significant improvement in the ordering of moves (> 10 per cent) or correct a fault observed in actual play.

The parameters used at present are:

(a) Material value

(b) Attacks on pieces by lower valued pieces or on inadequately defended pieces

(c) Attacks on defended pieces (helps build attacks)

(d) Hidden attacks: pins, x-rays, skewers

(e) Position of pieces (i.e. knights are weak at the edges of the board)

(f) Pawns increase in value as they advance

(g) Control of squares (central squares have a higher value)

(h) Doubling of rooks, queens and bishops

(i) Threats to squares next to the king

(j) Passed pawns increase in value rapidly as they advance

(k) Attacking passed pawns, the squares in front of passed pawns and blocking passed pawns

(l) The king is encouraged to go to knight 1 in the first part of the game and to move to the centre in the latter part (after half the material has gone for either side)

(m) Opposition of kings

(n) Moving kings together when the opponent has only a king. Without this a nine-ply program can have difficulty mating with king and

queen versus king, but with this even a five-ply program can mate with a
queen, a rook or two bishops and a king versus a king
(o) Keeping the king next to pawns
(p) Castling
This simple evaluation function has proved surprisingly good at ordering
the moves in certain types of game. A good example of this comes from
the game Reti *v*. Yates, N.Y. 1924. The position after sixteen moves is
shown in figure 5.

Figure 5. Reti vs Yates, New York 1924. The position after sixteen moves

The remaining moves of the game were then run through the move
ordering routine to see in what position it would order the master moves,
i.e. the order in which the moves would be handed to the tree searching
algorithm for further analysis. (N.B. This is the *static* ordering at *ply* 1.)
The results are shown in table 1.

Table 1.

	Reti move	total legal moves	position in list	Yates move	total legal moves	position in list
17	P–Q4	39	3	P–K5	45	2
18	N–K5	34	1	B × N	45	2
19	P × B	29	1	N–R2	39	3
20	P–B4	35	3	P × Pep	41	1
21	P × P	34	3	N–N4	40	2
22	P–B4	35	2	N–R6ch	43	1
23	K–R1	3	2	P–Q5	41	3
24	B × P	32	2	QR–Q1	46	7
25	R × B	37	3	P × R	38	1
26	B × BP	37	3	N–B7ch	36	3
27	K–N2	2	2	Q × B(Q5)	39	1
28	Q × Q	42	1	R × Q	31	1
29	B × R	39	1	N–K5	32	2
30	P–K6	39	10	R–Q7ch	33	1
31	K–B3	5	1	resigns		

Mean number of legal moves/position = 33.
Mean position of master move in list = 2.3.

TREE SEARCHING (3 to 19 plies, normally 7/9)

The moves are ordered at all but the final ply by the static evaluation. A mini-max search is then performed using $\alpha-\beta$ and, in the present version, a modified form of marginal forward pruning. The moves at the final ply are ordered by using the refutation technique. This basic order is then modified by the FEEDOVER table. These feedover trees are printed out by the program so that we can check what the program was 'thinking' about.

Figure 6. R. Maybury vs MASTER, 16.3.75. The position after 25 ... B–B2

Table 2 shows the feedover tree after move 25 of the game against R. Maybury; the corresponding board position is shown in figure 6. (See appendix 2 for the full game record.) The numbers correspond to the numbers of the squares on the board, i.e. 1 for bottom left and 64 for top right. The numbers go in pairs giving the square moved from and the square moved to for each side in turn. 0–0 means that the search of that branch has been terminated.

Table 2.

3–13	44–36	29–36	34–27	18–27	37–29	22–29	46–29
27–44	51–44	0–0	0–0	0–0	0–0	0–0	0–0
27–21	51–42	21–11	34–43	0–0	0–0	0–0	0–0
15–23	44–36	29–36	34–27	18–27	37–29	22–29	46–29
16–32	34–27	18–27	51–42	3–20	42–28	0–0	0–0
16–24	34–27	18–27	51–42	3–20	42–28	0–0	0–0
27–10	34–43	10–20	43–29	0–0	0–0	0–0	0–0
15–31	34–27	18–27	51–42	3–20	42–28	31–39	48–39
27–37	44–37	0–0	0–0	0–0	0–0	0–0	0–0
22–13	34–27	18–27	46–29	0–0	0–0	0–0	0–0
22–4	34–27	18–27	46–29	0–0	0–0	0–0	0–0
27–12	34–43	3–20	41–33	9–25	46–29	12–29	43–29
9–25	34–43	3–20	43–29	22–29	46–29	27–44	51–44
3–20	44–36	27–10	36–29	0–0	0–0	0–0	0–0
8–7	34–43	3–20	43–29	22–29	46–29	27–44	29–44
9–17	34–43	3–20	43–29	22–29	46–29	27–44	51–44
27–17	34–43	17–27	43–29	22–29	46–29	0–0	0–0

The 'best' line is always ordered to the top, i.e. the program expected its opponent to play 3–13 or N–K2. In fact its opponent played 3–20, i.e. N–Q3 which the program examined only to ply 5 as it considered that the move could be refuted by 26 ... P–Q4 27 N(4)–N2 P×P. The move P–Q4, which would have been examined third according to the static evaluation, was instead examined first because of feedover. Plies two and three looked first at N–N2 and P×P respectively. The move P–Q4 was finally selected after following the line down to nine plies.

Only two-replies to P–Q4 were examined to the full nine plies. A further twenty-two replies were considered of which none were searched beyond ply 5. The two lines were:

29–36	37–29	22–29	46–29	9–17	29–19	36–44	51–44
27–10	36–29	22–29	46–29	10–27	34–27	18–27	29–14

The program considered 29–36, i.e. P×P to be its opponent's best reply. This was in fact the move chosen.

Statistics for the game against R. Maybury

Mean number of moves at ply 1 examined by the tree searcher	14.0
Mean number of replies at ply 2 to 'best' ply 1 move	15.5
Mean position of move selected in ply 1 ordered list (without feedover)	3.1
Mean position of move selected in ply 1 ordered list (with feedover)	1.9
Mean position of opponent's move in feedover tree	3.7
Percentage of times feedover move was accepted	92%
Percentage of times opponent's move was considered best by MASTER	51%
Mean number of evaluations/sec.	903
Mean number of evaluations/move	40,220

It is difficult to give a meaningful estimate of the branching factor for the program, as many lines are cut before reaching the full search depth. However for the thirty-four moves examined with a seven-ply search, the mean number of nodes evaluated at the 7th ply was 9521. The seventh root of this gives a branching factor of 3.7. For the seven moves examined to nine plies the mean number of nodes examined at ply 9 was 32467. The ninth root of this gives a branching factor of 3.2. The search width is set much wider at plies 1 and 2 than at the other plies. It can be seen from the feedover trees that the moves are reasonable up to about five ply after which the moves get progressively wilder. This is partly due to heavier pruning at plies 7 and 8.

The game against P. Craske (see appendix 2) was the last one to show the tree pruning instability. Since then every move made by an opponent has been present in the feedover tree and therefore must have been examined to at least the third ply.

Appendix 2. Games

March 2 1975 White: Peter Craske (151) Black: MASTER

1	P–K4	P–QB4	Book
2	N–KB3	N–KB3	Book
3	N–QB3	P–Q3	Book
4	P–Q4	P×P	Book
5	N×P	P–QR3	Book
6	B–KN5	P–K3	Book
7	B–K2	B–Q2	36184	−71
8	0–0	B–K2	39845	−41
9	N–N3	B–B3	27683	−25
10	P–KB4	P–KR3	21315	−11
11	B×N	B×B	48209	11
12	P–K5	Q–N3+	2204	36
13	K–R1	P×P	44795	102
14	P–B5	0–0	46987	128
15	P×P	P×P	21873	40
16	B–N4	R–K1	84906	103
17	Q–K2	Q–N5	87847	98
18	P–QR3	Q–K2	109476	86
19	N–Q2	N–Q2	280420	113
20	QR–Q1	P–QR4	341015	87
21	N(2)–K4	N–B4	136152	62
22	N×B+	P×N	124929	72
23	B–R5	KR–Q1	48053	95
24	Q–N4+	K–R1	23086	80
25	Q–N6	R×R	16128	90

tree pruning instability

26	Q×RP+	Q–R2?	1207	132

tree pruning instability

27	Q×P+	Q–N2	36028	51
28	Q×Q+	K×Q	41	213
29	R×R	R–R1	18732	73
30	B–K2	P–K5	22305	69
31	B–N5	B×B	20403	76
32	N×B	P–R5	54772	65
33	R–K1	P–K4	28106	37
34	N–B3	R–R5?	20892	26
35	P–KN3	R–N5	24392	37
36	K–N2	K–B3	39555	−5

37	P–R3	R–N1	2623	−67	
38	N×P+	N×N	8975	−59	
39	R×N	R–QB1	20646	−70	
40	P–QB3	R–Q1	9469	−70	
41	K–B3	R–Q6+	11586	−44	
42	R–K3	R–Q7	22085	−55	
43	R–K2	R×R	8069	−64	
44	K×R	K–B4	18573	−92	
45	K–K3	K–N4	18204	−106	
46	K–K4	K–B3	3437	−132	
47	P–R4	P–N3	3534	−161	
48	P–B4	K–K3	3822	−196	
49	P–R5	K–B3	1730	−144	
50	P–R6	K–N3	1310	−145	
51	K×P	K×P	2970	−197	
52	K–Q5	K–N3	52246	−219	9 ply
53	K–B6	K–B4	33159	−208	
54	K×P	Resigns			

61 minutes CPU time. 570 nodes/second.

March 9 1975 White: MASTER Black: M. Duck (143)

1	N–KB3	P–QB4	Book	
2	P–KN3	P–Q4	Book	
3	B–N2	B–B4	9	71065
4	P–Q4	P–K3	34	138672
5	N–QB3	N–QB3	29	94905
6	P×P	KB×P	13	91894
7	N–KR4	KN–K2	−4	159565
8	N×B	N×N	−15	82554
9	P–K4	P×P	18	133597
10	Q×Q+	R×Q	−15	69187
11	N×P	B–N3	−11	93691
12	B–N5	R–Q2	−13	114897
13	P–KN4	N(4)–Q5	−15	158580
14	0–0–0	0–0	27	57499
15	P–QB3	N–K7+	22	21621
16	K–N1	R×R+	39	7148
17	R×R	P–B3	23	21849
18	B–K3	B×B	56	56572
19	P×B	P–B4	73	81219
20	P×P	P×P	132	27283
21	N–N5	R–K1	131	37164
22	B–Q5+	K–B1	251	6052
23	N–K6+	K–K2	166	3358
24	B×N	P×B	96	32072
25	N×P	R–KB1	65	14551
26	R–Q2	N–N8	72	49872

27	R–KB2	P–B5	110	50095	
28	P×P	N–R6	161	21929	
29	R–K2+	K–Q3	169	8267	
30	R–K6+	K–Q2	172	17265	
31	P–B5	R–B2	149	20732	
32	P–B6	N–N4	132	4812	
33	R–K7+	R×R	118	5815	
34	P×R	K×P	43	3987	
35	N–B5+	K–B3	50	8157	
36	N–Q4	P–B4	62	6111	
37	P–KR4	N–K5	55	6355	
38	N–QB6	P–QR3	49	22984	
39	K–B2	K–B4	60	22847	
40	P–N4	K–N5	65	22214	
41	N–K5+	K×P	60	5209	
42	K–Q3	N–B7+	55	47132	9 ply
43	K–K3	N–Q8+	39	11699	
44	K–Q2	N×P	102	28212	
45	K×N	P×P+	164	17281	
46	K×P	P–KR4	161	61654	
47	K–R5	K–N4	155	21492	
48	K×P	K–B4	169	19916	
49	N–B3	K–B5	194	27307	
50	N–N1?	P–R5	192	34121	

N–R4. No parameter for blocking passed pawns.

51	P–R4	K–N6	197	11829
52	K–N5	K–N7	203	5920
53	N–K2	K–B6	201	7457
54	N–Q4+	K–B7	203	18176
55	N–B5	P–R6	140	67909
56	N–R6	K–N6	−183	27006
57	N–B5+	K–B5	−194	42028
58	N–K7	P–R7	−253	62183
59	N–Q5+	K–B6	−285	48705
60	P–R5	P–R8(Q)	−267	86209
61	P–R6	Q–N8+	−273	155488
62	K–B5	Q–R7	−283	158795
63	N–N4	Q–R4+	−311	100711
64	K–B4	Q–N3	−306	121368
65	K–B3	K–K5	−316	147122
66	K–B4	K–K4	−298	166661
67	N–Q3+	K–Q3	−280	50246
68	N–N4	Q–B4+	−307	64913
69	K–N3	K–B2	−334	94349
70	N–Q3	Q–N4+	−369	128753
71	N–N4	K–N3	−377	57851
72	K–B3	Q–B4+	−368	50234

73	K–N3	K–N4	−372	121526
74	N–R2	Q–Q4+	−407	19313
75	K–R3	Q×N+!!	−404	45844
76	K×Q	K–B4!!	181	6

This was an experiment to see if the program could mate with a king and queen. It failed at 9 plies. When we encouraged the kings to come together it succeeded easily at 5 ply.

77	P–R7?	K–Q5	742	112001
78	P–R8(Q)	K–K4	773	276354
79	K–N3	K–Q5	788	354532
80	Q–KB3	K–B4	796	53054
81	K–B3	K–N4	828	48045
82	Q–Q5+	K–N3	884	33979
83	Q–Q6+	K–N4	910	15167
84	K–Q3	K–R5	898	27225
85	Q–B6+	K–N5	898	5931
86	Q–B4+	K–R4	898	4104
87	Q–B5+	K–R3	977	9027
88	Q–QN4	K–R2	985	9768
89	Q–N5	K–R1	1074	14680
90	Q–Q7	K–N1	1059	28417
91	Q–B6	K–R2	987	31597
92	K–K2	K–N1	988	14045
93	Q–Q7	K–R1	1074	19194
94	K–B2	K–N1	1064	34323
95	Q–B6	K–R2	986	24618
96	Q–N5	K–R1	1074	19066
97	K–K3	K–R2	988	30450
98	K–B4	K–R1	1074	23004
99	Q–N2	K–R2	988	14414
100	Q–R2+	K–N3	884	32009
101	Q–B4	K–R4	977	11321
102	Q–N3+	K–R3	1074	16259
103	Q–N4	K–R2	988	12078
104	Q–Q4+		985	10714

91 minutes CPU time. 961 nodes/second.

March 16 1975 White: Bob Maybury (143) Black: MASTER

1	P–K4	P–QB4	Book	
2	N–KB3	N–KB3	Book	
3	N–QB3	P–Q3	Book	
4	P–Q4	P×P	Book	
5	N×P	P–QR3	Book	
6	B–K2	P–K4	Book	
7	N–QN3	B–K2	Book	
8	B–KN5	0–0	26885	−18
9	0–0	QN–Q2	Book	

10	P–KB4	P–KR3	23119	−45
11	B×N	N×B	25846	−13
12	P–KB5	B–Q2	35776	2
13	B–KB3	R–QB1	20137	59
14	R–QB1	Q–QN3+	3886	89
15	K–KR1	Q–K6	47693	48
16	Q–Q2	Q×Q	20625	97
17	N×Q	R–QB2	48772	94
18	N–K2	KR–QB1	21077	86
19	P–QB4	P–QN4	37651	88
20	P×P	B×NP	12657	91
21	R×R	R×R	13932	65
22	R–QB1	R×R	11349	76
23	N×R	B–Q1	37716	71
24	P–QN3	B–QR4	6582	85

Change down depth = 9.

25	N–QB4	B–QB2	60594	43
26	N–Q3	P–Q4!	10838	95
27	P×P	P–K5	17933	92
28	B×P	N×B	119924	88
29	P–QR4	B–Q2	109048	80
30	P–KN4	P–KB3	127725	79
31	K–KN2	K–KB2	321496	95

Switching back to 7 (timer error).

32	K–KB3	N–KN4+	34768	100
33	K–KN2	N–K5	115977	100
34	K–KB3	N–QB6	18114	95

Should have taken the draw. (No! Black can still win—Ed.)

35	N–QB5	K–K2	13068	74	
36	N×P	B×KRP	19563	92	
37	N–QN4	B–QB2	49178	82	B–N8 better?
38	P–QR5	P–KR4	25343	85	
39	P–QR6	P×P+	11743	96	
40	K×P	P–KN3??	29790	136	

N–N4 idiot! Still trying to win material.

41	P–R7	B×P+	17817	−58
42	K–KB3	B–K5+	21937	−55
43	K–KB2	N–Q8+	27068	−167
44	K–K1	B–KN6+	17404	−177
45	K×N	B–KB6+	9382	−285

Horizon effect??

46	K–Q2	B–KB5+	9094	−374	
47	N–K3	K–KB1	18303	−460	Waffling now.
48	P–R8(Q)+	K–KN2	32388	−470	
49	N–Q3	Resigns			

30 minutes CPU time. 900 nodes/second.

The complete moves of the game between MASTER (White) and Dr Hans
Berliner (222), Sunday 23 March, 1975.

			secs	value
1	N–KB3	N–QB3	0	0
2	P–QB4	P–K4	24	25
3	P–Q4	P–K5	57	27
4	N–K5!	Q–B3	24	31
5	N×N	QP×N	22	28
6	N–B3	B–KB4	56	34
7	B–K3	0–0–0	163	60
8	Q–R4	P–QR3	105	88
9	0–0–0	N–R3	65	85
10	P–B3!	Q–K2	58	46
11	Q–R5	P–KN3	17	99
12	Q–K5?	Q×Q	21	90
13	P×Q	R×R+	2	57
14	K×R	B–K3	10	51
15	N×P	N–KB4	45	43
16	B–B4	B×P	40	38
17	P–QN3	B–Q4	41	52
18	N–B6	B–K3	24	63
19	P–K4	N–Q5	47	40
20	B–Q2??	B–QR6!	43	15
21	B–QB4	B×B	38	10
22	P×B	R–Q1	29	29
23	K–K1	P–KR4	74	19
24	K–B2	N×P	50	34
25	B–B1	B×B	38	−29
26	K×N	R–Q6+	1	−35
27	K–K2	R–Q7+	7	−56
28	K–B3	B–N7	22	−84
29	K–K3	R×P	103	−110
30	K–B4	R–QB7	27	−111
31	R–Q1	R–B6	39	−109
32	K–N5	R×P	26	−100
33	R–Q7	B×P	10	−97
34	R×P	B×N+	6	−89
35	K×B	R×P	5	−95
36	R–B8+	K–Q2	6	−113
37	K×P	R–KR5	105	−121
38	R–B7+	K–Q3	6	−71

O: A couple of moves and resign ... OK?
M: Fine by me—this is a difficult one to win.

			secs	value
39	R–B6+	K–Q4	25	−103
40	R–B5+	K–Q5	175	−104
41	R–B2! and resigns		189	−123

A Quantitative Study of King and Pawn Against King

M. R. B. Clarke

At this final stage of the meeting I would like to end on a purifying and uplifting note by considering only programs that play perfectly.

On the whole, and with the exception of theorem proving which is a rather different thing, people working in AI have approached real and difficult problems such as chess by hacking away with the most appropriate tools they can lay their hands on to produce the best result they can. I am going to argue that this may be good practical engineering but it is nevertheless bad science. Such methods usually involve embedding knowledge in software, making measurement of the amount required to carry out a given task difficult, and although comparison of the results with those of numerically graded human performers may be the best we can do at present in the opening and middlegame, in the endgame at least we can and should aim at perfection.

Tan's (1972) program for king and pawn against king (KPK) is a good example of both the strength and weakness of the traditional AI approach. It consists of a meticulous transcription of chess knowledge from books written by outstanding human players into a programming language (POP-2) that is well suited to the task. The result is a program that plays very well indeed—no mean feat. No one knows if it plays perfectly—indeed no one has discussed whether it matters if it doesn't. The point of the exercise was to see how effectively (in purely qualitative and essentially unquantifiable terms) human knowledge could be expressed as procedures in machine executable software in contrast to 'flattening' all this knowledge on to one dimension by numerical weighting of heuristics (which is known to be a totally ineffective method in the endgame). The limitation of this approach is that it is only self-extending as far as results and not methods are concerned, by which I mean that although one could use Tan's KPK program as a terminal node evaluator for a more complicated ending, K and 2P vs K and P for example, the extra knowledge required would again have to be laboriously coded in POP-2 by an expert chess player and programmer.

In saying all this I am not of course intending to adversely criticise Tan's work—quite the reverse, I am singling it out as the most relevant so far. What I am doing is to put forward the view that we now need to study in a more scientific way the problem of why it is difficult to write effective computer programs for chess endings. Is it because there are lots of special cases? Is it because there are general patterns in winning positions that we lack a formalism for describing? To answer such questions we need to treat the endings more specifically as a computational problem whose complexity we can study in a controlled and quantitative way.

First of all, what can we say about the way people play KPK? Undoubtedly there are some who play the ending perfectly, although not as many as one might think. (If you believe you are one of them try the examples in figures 1, 2 and 3!) Even without doing a properly designed psychological experiment it is safe to say that we use a combination of lookahead and lookup in a goal-directed way. Variations are explored which force transitions to classes of position whose result is known to be as favourable as possible. It is also, I think, safe to assume that the better the player the less lookahead and more lookup he does. Lookahead (for people) involves mental calculation and is therefore slow and error-prone; the ideal balance will not necessarily be the same for machines. Eliminating one of the variables by considering only programs that play perfectly (in a sense to be made clear below) the remaining elements, lookahead and lookup, are both accessible to a quantitative study.

To start with we can think of two extreme types of program at opposite ends of a time/store trade-off axis:

lot of computing	little computing
small memory	large memory

At the left-hand end we have the program that carries out for a given position the complete $\alpha-\beta$ search to termination. Not only is this quite a simple program in the sense of being embodied in a rather small amount of code, but it also uses no store for data. The only 'knowledge' it has is the definition of terminal positions and the irreducible minimum representing the rules of the game. This simplicity is paid for in computing time, which will rise exponentially with distance from the terminal nodes.

At the other end of the scale we have an even simpler program which for a given position merely looks up its value and the best move to achieve it. It is tempting to call this program RETI in view of the well-known anecdote about the lady who asked the master Reti: 'How many moves do you look ahead?' to which he is reputed to have replied 'One—the right one'. Actually I have never thought that this rang quite true. Reti was by all accounts a modest man and the alternative version that attributes the starring role to the bombastic Bogoljubov sounds more plausible. However for present purposes Reti begins with R and can therefore give his name to the right-hand end of the time/store axis. The left-hand end we need to dedicate to someone who believes that AI will founder in the face of the ultimate deterrent of the combinatorial explosion and whose name begins with L. I shall leave this as an exercise for the satirically-minded reader.

RETI of course needs a good memory. How large will it have to be? The crudest possible answer gives 64 possibilities for each piece resulting in 2^{18} different configurations of the three pieces. Clearly this can be reduced considerably by perceiving that the pawn can never change files and never be on the first rank. Using this symmetry about the mid-line and confining the pawn to files a–d gives $7 \times 4 \times 4096 = 114\,688$ possible configurations, each of which can be given a unique code or coordinate in a canonical state space

$$c = 16384\,(P_r - 2) + 4096(P_f - 1) + 512(w_r - 1) +$$
$$+ 64(w_f - 1) + 8(B_r - 1) + (B_f - 1)$$

where P_r and P_f are the pawn's rank and file, (2–8) and (1–4) respectively, and w and b refer similarly to the white and black kings.

Of these 114 688 positions a simple calculation shows that 16 696 are impossible in the sense that pieces are on top of, or kings next to, each other, these impossible positions being irregularly distributed through the canonical state space. Each of the remaining positions can be thought of as having two values, win or draw for White to move, loss or draw for Black, which may of course be different. A table storing only these win or draw values would not always be sufficient to deduce the best move, and yet to actually store a best move leads to difficulties in the many cases where there is more than one.

The simplest solution is to store a value and a depth for each side to move, these being defined as the mini-max values, where White chooses the shortest path win and longest draw and Black the opposite. The most efficient way to compute these is by backing-up breadth-first from the terminal positions because then the wins for White and draws for Black are evaluated as soon as they can be.

For KPK I do this by maintaining for every configuration c a twenty-bit word consisting of an eleven-bit part $w(c)$—one bit for each of the ten possible white moves from c plus an 'evaluated' marker bit—and a similar nine-bit part $B(c)$ for Black. This file is initialised by setting bits corresponding to illegal moves for both sides in every configuration, and by evaluating the terminal positions, which are all defined with Black to move. Depth zero losses for Black are those positions where $P_r = 8$ and either b does not attack P, or he does but w defends P (there are 12 985 of these). Depth zero draws are slightly more complicated. Either b can take P on the move (10 093 positions) or Black is stalemated (nine of these, not counting of course those where White can promote to a rook to avoid stalemate!), or Black can move to one of the two positions where White is stalemated (seven of these). Depth zero wins for White are those where he can legally transform the position to a depth zero loss for Black, depth zero draws for White those where he cannot avoid transforming to a depth zero draw for Black. For convenience I disregard positions with $P_r = 8$ when White is to move (leaving 98 304 out of the full 114 688) and set the two white stalemates as illegal, as of course are positions where Black is in check with White on the move.

The breadth-first backing up then goes as follows. Suppose c' is a configuration that has just been evaluated as a win for White with Black to move at depth d, and that c is a typical configuration with White to move obtained by retracting a white move in c'. Then if c has not yet been evaluated at lower depth it can be marked as a win at depth d in the certainty that this is the quickest win at c, and $w(c)$ is set to $1024+2d+1$. Alternatively if c' is a draw with Black to move then we set the bit in $w(c)$ corresponding to the white move from c to c' and test $w(c)$ against 1023. If $w(c) = 1023$ then White cannot avoid the draw at c and the last one found is the longest (depth d); $w(c)$ is then set to $1024+2d+2$. $w(c) = 1024$ indicates that c is impossible or illegal (Black in check, say).

A similar procedure is used to evaluate Black-to-move position at depth $(d+1)$ by backing up from all those evaluated for White at depth d. Eventually no more positions can be evaluated while many for both Black and White to move are left unevaluated. These are positions which transform into each other in cycles, for example when Black has the opposition, and when White can only break the loop by relinquishing the pawn or allowing stalemate. Table 1 shows the frequency distribution of positions evaluated at each depth. Depth zero for Black are terminal positions, and for white positions that can be transformed to terminals on the move.

Table 1.

depth	Black to move		White to move	
	draws	losses	draws	wins
0	10 109	12 985	2 730	12 749
1	6 156	11 278	3 243	11 300
2	5 454	9 513	2 765	9 624
3	3 172	7 604	1 405	7 864
4	1 396	5 729	504	10 511
5	438	5 777	130	2 564
6	59	1 982	0	1 416
7	0	1 433	0	1 457
8	0	1 315	0	1 122
9	0	966	0	941
10	0	795	0	685
11	0	597	0	670
12	0	560	0	586
13	0	502	0	572
14	0	481	0	307
15	0	213	0	78
16	0	36	0	22
17	0	15	0	8
18	0	4	0	3
19	0	2	0	0
∞	9 421		8 406	
total	36 205	61 787	19 183	62 479
	drawn	36 205	drawn	19 183
	impossible	16 696	impossible	14 292
			Black in check	2 348
			stalemate	2
grand total		114 688		98 304

In the longest solutions therefore White queens (or 'rooks' to avoid stalemate) in a maximum of nineteen moves; draws either occur by repetition (depth ∞), as when Black gets the opposition, or by Black capturing the pawn, which must happen if at all in seven moves or less. Detecting impossible positions separately, and omitting those with the pawn on the 8th rank, there are 27 possible values for each side to move, giving 729 values to be stored for each configuration. A simple counting program shows that only 262 of these pairs actually occur and only 252 more than once. If six of these single positions are detected separately the final reckoning for the size of database that RETI needs is 98 304 configurations requiring eight bits of store each, or 786 432 bits in all, plus the simple program to access them. This has been implemented to work on-line on the 1904s at Queen Mary College, and it will either print-out all the depth and best move statistics for a given position or actually play the ending perfectly and instantaneously against an opponent.

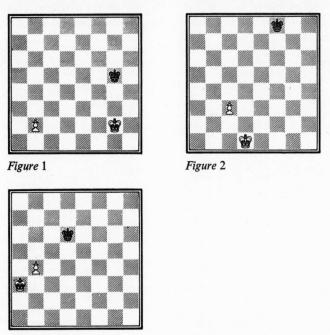

Figure 1   *Figure* 2

Figure 3. White to play and win in each case

Not many K P K positions are particularly difficult or even interesting to good players, who have of course mastered the relevant concepts, but to the less strong player the ending does present some difficulties. Some of the more interesting positions are shown in figures 1, 2 and 3. Figure 1 is just one of the three longest solutions (the other two are with the w K on h2 and h3) where White takes 19 moves to queen starting by taking the opposition with 1 Kg3. Figure 2 is more interesting and causes all but the best players some trouble. It is a good illustration of the concept of key squares (in this case b5, c5 and d5) where White's winning method is not quite so obvious. The only way to win is 1 кc2 кe7 2 кb3 кd6 3 кb4! (ensuring that he gets the opposition) ... кc6 4 кc4 etc. (White queens on move 14).

Figure 3 is a nice example, the first position in Lommer (1975), where the sting is in the tail. 1 кa4 кc6 2 кa5 кb7 3 кb5 кa7 4 кc6 кa6 5 b5ch кa7 6 кc7 кa8 and now not 7 b6 stalemate, but 7 кb6 кb8 8 кa6! кa8 9 b6 taking the opposition and winning in the usual way after 9 ... кb8 10 b7 кc7 11 кa7 etc.

So much then for the full state-space look-up program and its statistics. I now go on to consider ways of using it to improve the efficiency of this computation.

The point at which any particular device, whether human or electronic, chooses to operate on the time/store axis depends on its processing speed, retrieval time and store capacity and is not worth pursuing further here. What is important is how the size of RETI's memory can be reduced without making any compromise on the standard of play. Obviously people don't memorise every position in the complete state space; they recognise that in many cases it is not the particular squares the pieces are on that determines the outcome but the pattern of their relative position, which may be invariant over many different configurations. It makes no difference for example in many cases whether the white pawn is on the c or d files; White can push it through or Black draw with precisely the same sequence of moves, provided that they are described in terms of variables rather than constants. On the other hand it is not always so simple, even here there are exceptions since Black can be stalemated in the corner with the pawn on the c file.

Is there then a smaller yet value-preserving system of patterns on to which the state space can be mapped? One can attempt to answer this question by trying to generate such a system and comparing it with the complete state space file that we already have. Exceptions or discrepancies will have to be dealt with by defining new classes to take complete account of them. Short of doing all this it is difficult to predict in advance how great the reduction will be, although it will clearly be substantial. The obvious starting point is from the definitions of primitive positions, which are already specified in a most economical pattern code.

From the simple definition of a loss for Black at depth zero as
[primitive loss for Black] =
    [position legal] ∧ [Black to move]
    ∧ [pawn on 8th rank] ∧ [[Black not attacking pawn]
    ∨ [[Black attacking pawn] ∧ [White defending it]]]
we can deduce that a win for White at depth zero is completely specified by the pattern
[win for White at depth zero by pushing pawn] =
    [position legal] ∧ [White to move] ∧ [pawn on 7th rank]
    ∧ [Black king not occupying queening square]
    ∧ [White king not occupying queening square]
    ∧ [[Black not attacking queening square] ∨

∨ [[Black attacking queening square]
∧ [White defending it]]]

and this process of backing up in pattern space can clearly be continued up the tree, provided that the repertoire of descriptions out of which the predicates are formed is suitably enriched as, and only as, necessary.

Patterns are then functions formed from predicates, taking configurations in state space as arguments, such that all positions which fit the pattern have the same value and require the same action (in terms of transformation to a simpler pattern). It is fairly certain from human experience that a data-base for KPK coded in such a pattern space will be considerably more economical than that in state space, even allowing for the time required to compute the predicates, but this is a question that can only be settled by actually doing it, and examining carefully the exceptional cases, which must all be accounted for since it is important that no compromise on optimality is made.

Clearly the ultimate aim is to get the machine itself to back up in pattern space generating new predicates and descriptions as required in as economical a way as possible. This is not going to be easy; the synthesis of new descriptions is nothing more or less than the function-building problem, albeit on a restricted chess-specific basis set.

The first step will be to carry on as above generating patterns by hand, but using the machine to make comparisons for correctness and completeness against the full state-space file. At each stage the pattern coding can be iteratively refined by detecting and eliminating exceptions until it is perfectly correct at a given depth before backing up another ply. Of course although the clerical labour of looking for anomalies between the current pattern coding and the state-space file will have been mechanised at this stage the patterns themselves will have to be refined in an ad hoc way by the programmer, who should nevertheless in doing so have his eye firmly on eventual automation, and be conscious of the need for the predicates and descriptions that he uses to be generated in a clean, tree-structured way from a well-defined set of basic elements.

Perhaps I should end by trying to relate all this to some other AI work.

Tan's program I have mentioned above. In a sense he has already arrived at a coding for KPK but it contains elements of lookahead and is not in a form that lends itself to either quantitative analysis or automatic extension. Neither is it known to be perfectly correct; it would be interesting indeed to make a comparison against the data-base. Elcock and Murray (1968) wrote a description-synthesizing program for Go-moku but it only worked on samples and did not attempt a complete analysis of the game. Unfortunately, for some reason, doubtless unconnected with the problem itself, they seem never to have pushed their work as far as it might have gone.

I'm not sure that what I have been discussing above should be called 'learning' or 'induction' in the common AI usage of these terms, although I am perhaps talking about 'concept formation'. In the usual formulation of induction (e.g. Popplestone 1969) we present the machine with a *sample* of the input-output table and ask it to generate predicates or functions of the state-space description common to all members of the sample. In this context we might show it a collection of positions all won for White because he has the opposition and hope that its function-building algorithm homes in on this as the relevant geometric feature.

What we aim at here is something rather different, seemingly deductive rather than inductive in that we *prove* that the opposition is the relevant geometric feature by backing up from *all* situations one level simpler. There is however a much more interesting problem well known to psychologists and considered rather difficult: how is it that people can 'get the idea' from one example? To be more specific suppose that in the process of backing-up we have found that White wins if he controls a certain square, such as c6 in figure 2. He can do this by occupying one of the key squares b5, c5, d5, of which Black can only defend all three from c6 (a *theorem* in the geometry of the chess-board) and White can only move to all three from c4. Therefore, the reasoning goes, if Black occupies c6 White must occupy c4 with Black to move—hence the opposition. It seems to me that the human player uses the example here as a diagram to suggest chess theorems for which he then finds a proof in much the same way as he might in geometry, whereas in the usual kind of induction from a partial or complete sample the comparative lack of direction in the function-building algorithm will always condemn such methods to only partial success unless there is some underlying formalism within which chess theorems can be proved.

REFERENCES

Averbakh, Y. (1966) *Chess Endings: Essential Knowledge.* Pergamon Press.

Fine, R. (1941) *Basic Chess Endings.* Bell.

Lommer, H. M. (1975) 1357 *End-game Studies.* Pitman.

Murray, A. M. & E. W. Elcock (1968) Automatic description and recognition of board patterns in go-moku, in *Machine Intelligence 2* (eds Dale & Michie) 75–88. Edinburgh University Press.

Popplestone, R. J. (1969) An experiment in automatic induction, in *Machine Intelligence 5* (eds Meltzer & Michie) 203–15. Edinburgh University Press.

Tan, S. T. (1972) Representation of knowledge for very simple pawn endings in chess. *Research Memo MIP-R-98*, Department of Machine Intelligence, University of Edinburgh.

Appendix. King and Rook against King

In view of Michie's paper in this volume I thought it would be interesting to carry out a similar statistical study of KRK. In this case, although we also have three pieces, the problem is rather simpler because Black can never draw at depths greater than zero and the state space is smaller because there are more symmetries. A canonical representation is obtained by up to three reflections about the horizontal, vertical and diagonal mid-lines of the board which bring the black king (B) to one of the ten squares a1, b1, c1, d1, b2, c2, d2, c3, d3, d4. When B is on the diagonal a1, b2, c3, d4 the white king (W) can be reflected into the lower triangle, and when W is on the diagonal the white rook (R) can be reflected into the lower triangle. This gives 32896 possible configurations of which 4840 have pieces on top of each other or kings adjacent leaving 28056 to be evaluated. Again terminal positions can be defined with Black to move, the wins (for White) being the 27 mates, and the draws the nine stalemates and all configurations where the rook is *en prise*.

Table 2.

depth	Black to move	White to move	
0	27	189	
1	78	587	
2	246	484	
3	81	238	
4	198	607	
5	471	1091	
6	592	1418	
7	683	2149	
8	1433	2514	
9	1712	2382	
10	1985	2565	
11	2854	2691	
12	3597	2234	
13	4194	2027	
14	4553	662	
15	2166	121	
16	390	0	
total	25233	21959	
rook *en prise*	2787	6097	where Black is in check
stalemate	9		
	28056	28056	

Evaluation of the remaining positions is done by breadth-first backing-up exactly as for K P K except of course that a record of evaluated transformations need only be kept for Black to move. The results are shown in table 2, where again I show for each depth the number of positions which resulted in minimum/maximum-path wins for White/Black at that depth. Depth zero for Black means that he is mated in that position and for White that he can mate on the move.

Certainly the most (and probably the only) significant feature of this table is that it shows White to have a mate in a maximum of sixteen moves from any configuration, whereas no less an authority than Fine (1941) states that in the position of figure 4 White needs sixteen moves, and in the same position but with the rook on b2 instead of b1 White needs seventeen moves to force the mate.

Figure 4. According to Fine (1941) White needs sixteen moves to mate from this position

To find out where Fine went wrong I set up a table look-up program for KRK similar to that discussed above and ran his solution through it. Table 3 gives Fine's mating sequence and, after the initial position and

Table 3.

Position of figure 4			depth 14
1	Kb2	Kd4	depth 13
2	Kc2	Ke4	depth 13
3	Kc3	Ke5	depth 12
4	Kc4	Ke4	depth 11
5	Re1ch	Kf5	depth 10
6	Kd4	Kf4	depth 9
7	Rf1ch	Kg5	depth 8
8	Ke4	Kg6	depth 7
9	Ke5	Kg5	depth 6
10	Rg1ch	Kh4	depth 5
11	Kf5	Kh3	depth 4
12	Kf4	Kh2	depth 3
13	Rg3	Kh1	depth 2
14	Kf3	Kh2	depth 1
15	Kf2	Kh1	depth 0
16	Rh3 mate		

each move of Black, the minimal path depths printed out by the KRK program. Clearly Fine's error lies in playing 2 Kc2 and in fact one can easily use the program to establish that better moves are either 2 Kb3 or 2 Re1, both of which mate in one move less.

It is also interesting to find that Averbakh (1966) apparently reproduces Fine's non-optimal solution without noticing the error.

Finally perhaps it is worth remarking for future comparison on the amount of memory required for the RETI-type table-look-up program used to get these results. For White-to-move positions there are 17 possibilities, 16 depth values and an illegality marker; for Black there are 19, 17 depths, draw, or illegal. Of the 17×19 ($= 323$) possibilities for each configuration only 158 in fact occur so that we can easily get three table entries in a 24-bit integer word, making a total memory requirement of 10966 words. This, of course, will be substantially reduced by a successful pattern coding of the kind described in Michie's paper, and the computation involved in backing up in pattern space will be correspondingly more efficient. What will be interesting is again to see the extent to which refinement of the pattern coding can be made an automatic part of the backing-up algorithm.